MYSTERY, MAGIC, AND MEDICINE

MYSTERY, MAGIC, AND MEDICINE

THE RISE OF MEDICINE FROM SUPERSTITION TO SCIENCE

By

HOWARD W. HAGGARD, M.D.

Associate Professor of Applied Physiology
Yale University

Author of *Devils, Drugs, and Doctors;*
The Lame, the Halt, and the Blind;
The Science of Health
and Disease, etc.

Doubleday, Doran & Company, Inc.
Garden City, New York
1933

PRINTED AT THE *Country Life Press*, GARDEN CITY, N. Y., U. S. A.

AUTHOR'S NOTE

THERE is probably no more fascinating story than that of the rise of scientific medicine. Its beginnings were in mystery and superstition; its progress encumbered with ignorance and quackery. Above these it has risen to become the most beneficent science of the modern world.

The story of medicine is that of a long and difficult struggle with the mysteries of life; a struggle which has brought about astounding achievements in the prevention and cure of disease, amelioration of human suffering and prolongation of life.

In the past medicine had its place only at the bedside of the individual patient. Today medical science has transcended these narrow limits and has become a guiding force in modern civilization. But, in becoming such, medicine has enlisted to its aid every agency of our society, even to the participation of the individual citizen. To him, the citizen, I recommend particularly the pages describing these modern developments, for they tell of the part that he has played in the struggle against disease.

The period of modern ascendancy of medical science covers only some seventy-five years. These years encompass such discoveries as the bacterial cause of infection, one of the greatest triumphs in man's struggle against his environment. None of equal medical importance antecede it and only two from an earlier period approach it: Jenner's demonstration of vaccination against smallpox and the discovery of Long and Wells and Morton of the possibilities of producing anesthesia for surgical operation.

But discoveries such as these with all of their beneficent possibilities are of no practical usefulness unless they are put into application. Of what benefit is the knowledge of the cause of infection unless that knowledge is used in the hospital and in the home and built into the sanitary codes of our cities? Jenner's discovery would save no one from smallpox if vaccine virus were not available to the physician. The mere fact that ether produces anesthesia brings no relief from pain to the patient undergoing operation. Ether, suitable for anesthesia, must be available to the surgeon; it has been made available only by co-operation. In each field there have been pioneers, and it is to one of these I wish to pay tribute—to a scientist, who, in his dual capacity of physician and chemist, perceived the necessity for such coöperation, and devoted his life to effecting it; and to perpetuate his work, founded, seventy-five years ago, the Laboratories which bear his name.

I dedicate this book to the memory of Dr. E. R. SQUIBB, a pioneer in the advancement of scientific medicine.

HOWARD W. HAGGARD.

New Haven, Conn.
November, 1933.

MYSTERY, MAGIC, AND MEDICINE: IN THE BEGIN-
ning they were one and the same. And the healing
methods that thousands of years ago sprang up and
were developed by one group of primitive savage
people were the same type as those developed by all
others. In principle they are the same kind that are
practiced today by native peoples in the fastness of
Africa and in all other remote and uncivilized regions.

For primitive, or ancient, medicine is the expression of a philosophy that grows from the natural
reactions of all ignorant men placed in hazardous
surroundings. In the early days, long before civilization had developed, savage man was not, as some
people believe, a carefree creature living a free and
idealistic life in the midst of an abundant Eden. Instead, this ancient ancestor of ours was a terror-
driven, ignorant savage facing a hostile world. By day
he slunk through the rough woods in search of food,
in constant fear of death by stronger men and beasts.
In the dark he hid from unseen terrors, and in his
nakedness he shivered in the cold of night. He

trembled before the lightning and fell prostrate before the thunder. When convulsed in the agony of disease, he hid like a dumb beast. Injured, he crawled to his lair to die of hunger or be murdered by ruthless enemies.

Even as he crouched and shivered in a world to which he was illy suited physically, he sought an explanation for his plight. He was ignorant, but he was intelligent. The mere fact that he developed mysteries established him as man, for no other animal has ever had the intelligence to reason on abstract matters.

The man of primitive times looked upon a world which terrified him. Like a child frightened by darkness he peopled the world about him with creatures of his imagination. These intangible reflections of his mind he called spirits and ghosts. For all the phenomena that he could not understand in the world about him these imaginary beings, so he believed, were responsible. One such phenomenon was disease.

In the childhood of the race man did not sift the facts before him, dispassionately searching for their relations. Such an attitude was developed only when he no longer feared his surroundings. We can almost trace the very thoughts that went through the mind of primitive man as he evolved his philosophy of life, for being men, we tend to think as he did, even though we have modified this tendency with training and education. And being egotistical ourselves, it is easy for us to comprehend the conceit of the savage. We know his desire to believe that the things he successfully accomplished were due to his own sterling efforts. We sympathize with him for wanting to believe as well that his misfortunes, his ill luck, were due to no fault of his own. But at this point we differ, for he attributed these misfortunes to supernatural forces, to the spirits and the ghosts with which he had peopled the world. They and they alone were responsible. And as disease was one of his misfortunes, it, like all others, was ascribed to supernatural malevolent forces.

Primitive man, looking upon the world about him, saw things in motion. Trees swayed in the breeze; leaves rustled; waters ran in the rivers; clouds floated overhead; and the sun and moon seemed to traverse the heavens; animals and men moved. Now animals and men were alive. They had spirits, for he saw them in his dreams as he slept. Hence, by his reasoning, it followed that the trees, and water, and clouds, and sun, and moon were alive too and possessed living spirits, as did men and animals.

Such personification of inanimate things is a way of thinking that all children have. The little boys and girls of today at play or at their story books, when they talk or read of speaking bears, and singing trees, and whispering winds are mimicking in their way the serious thoughts of savage man in the childhood of the race.

Spirits—supernatural forces—bring disease and all other misfortune; that was, and still is, the belief of savage man. To prevent or cure disease the spirits must be controlled, either forced away or bribed to leave. That is the theory his remedial practice rests upon.

We today can trace the development of the practice from the earliest times. Then some individuals among the savages of the tribe were shrewder, cleverer men than the rest; or perhaps they were not quite so normal as the others, a little queer. At any rate they were not well understood by the others, who came to believe that they had power over the spirits, the mysterious forces that sent the sunshine and the rain, that brought game to the hunter and gave success in combat. Such a man was the one, then, to whom the others turned for relief from the spirits that brought disease. He was the medicine man. Unfortunately, but logically, these earliest physicians were expected not only to heal their friends but to cast sickness upon their enemies as well. They practiced what we should call both white magic (healing magic) and black magic (destructive magic).

As centuries went on, tribal organizations grew, and these medicine men, who were priests as well as doctors, became a special group whom only the elect might join. They had ceremonies and initiations and customs and rites, but that stage of development brings us very near to the healing priests of early civilization. Let us pause first for a moment to see how the savage medicine men carried out their duties as physicians, for remnants of their practices we shall find in ancient civilizations—and even in our own.

The basic philosophy of primitive medicine was uniform throughout all the early peoples; they believed that supernatural forces caused disease. But they developed many different ceremonies for overcoming these forces. The remnants of their rites are the superstitions of today. But let us recognize that these practices were not superstitions in early days; they have become so only since we have gained knowledge. Superstition implies practices that are derived logically but from premises which are *not* consistent with generally prevailing knowledge. When a savage sees his image in a mirror, knowing nothing of optics, he thinks that it is his spirit he sees—his soul. If, then, he breaks the mirror, he believes quite logically that he has injured his soul, an unlucky thing to do. He is not superstitious; he is simply ignorant. His logic is good; it is his premise that is bad. But when knowledge of the principles of optics has become available and general and we have learned that the reflection is not the soul, then to believe that breaking a mirror brings bad luck no longer has a premise consistent with generally prevailing knowledge. It has become a mere superstition.

The most general practice of the savage medicine man was a crude variety of what we today should call psychotherapy—a treatment that has its influence upon the mind of the patient. For example, the medicine man in treating his patient often ostensibly tried to frighten the spirits away. He put on a costume that was bizarre and fantastic. He danced and shouted before his patient, shaking a rattle. As a result of this procedure the patient seemed actually to improve in health. And he did, temporarily. But the cause of this improvement was the influence of the patient's mental processes upon his bodily functions. As long as he sincerely believed that the medicine man was driving away the spirits, the pain was eased and anxiety dispelled. He *felt* better.

Some of the patients actually were cured. They were either those whose ailments were mental in the beginning or those who, thanks to the enormous recuperative powers of the human body, would have got well anyway. But the medicine man did not discriminate. Neither did his followers. The so-called controlled experiment in science is of very recent origin. Statistics are a modern institution. But very old, deeply ingrained in human thinking, is the habit of drawing false conclusions, a habit which is described by the Latin phrase, *Post hoc; ergo propter hoc* (After it; therefore because of it).

The medicine man treated his patients. Many of them got well. Hence, by this very common way of thinking, they got well because of the treatment.

This type of thinking is the basis for all the ancient medical practices—now discarded—and also for the quackery and healing cults and fads of today. The latter, without exception, are direct revivals or modifications or applications of the false reasoning of another day. It is the function of modern scientific

Blood-letting as depicted by Peytel

medicine to investigate all methods of treatment and to discard those which have no real value, for if confidence is placed upon such false methods of healing, disaster follows when they are applied to serious illness.

The ways in which the medicine man attempted to drive away the spirits were almost infinite in number, and each, of course, worked equally well as long as the patient had confidence. But it was in trying things for their effect on the actual presence of the spirits that remedies from animal, vegetable, and mineral sources came into use. The overwhelming majority were useless, of course, but a few that were stumbled upon had such real medicinal value that they are still in beneficial use today for definite and selected purposes. Others are carried on as home remedies by the superstitious or fostered by quacks.

Many of the remedial substances of presumed or real value were employed only after civilization had made a definite start. Into that early civilization was carried over with no change in principle, however, the philosophy which primitive man had developed—the philosophy that maintained that disease was a spiritual matter. Formal religion had arisen, and religion likewise deals with spiritual matters. So, as we move along to the medicine of early civilization, it is not surprising that we find mystery and magic and medicine now becoming religion and magic and medicine. From the savage medicine man was evolved the pagan priest.

Religion Enters the Field of Medicine

THE Code of Hammurabi shows us that the practice of medicine was regulated by the Babylonians as far back as 2250 B.C. One of the most ancient medicines of civilized peoples of which we have definite knowledge is that of Egypt, the Egypt of 4000 to 5000 years ago. Medicine then was a mixture of what we should call superstition and religion, on the one hand, and also, on the other, very practical measures. The

Hippocrates, about 460–371 B.C., the father of modern medicine.

ancient Egyptians carried out religious healings by invocations to the Gods; they administered medicinal substances, most of which had no virtue but some few of which did; and they performed surgical operations of a crude sort, splinted broken limbs. Today the ancient inscriptions exist which tell of the numerous medicaments and the often absurd compounding used by the Egyptians.

In passing let us pause a moment to see why people used medicaments. Animals, you know, were often deeply respected, even worshipped, by ancient peoples —the sacred animals of Egypt, the totem animals of the tribes of North America. Animals were assumed to have certain virtues which might be preserved and absorbed into the bodies of humans. Sometimes, therefore, they were sacrificed and eaten; sometimes they were allowed to die before their flesh was reverently consumed. Thus the lungs of the fox, a long-winded animal, were thought to be good for consumption; and the fat of a bear, since it was a hairy animal, was considered efficacious in the treatment of baldness. Eating a lion's heart—or, in truth, the heart of a brave human enemy—was supposed to yield courage. From such ideas it is not a far stretch to the belief, even now persisting, that "goose grease" has an especial virtue as an ointment for bronchitis, or that rattlesnake oil, or even that of earth worms, rubbed on the skin makes an athlete limber.

To old folk-legend we owe at least one very valuable animal remedy—cod liver oil; it has been used for centuries, but only in the last few years, since the discovery of the vitamins, has science demonstrated the amazing benefits to be derived from it. Furthermore, in ancient times toads were boiled up, as in the witches' caldrons, and were used to treat heart disease and dropsy; modern science, curiously enough, has shown that the skin of a toad contains a substance essentially similar in action to digitalis and therefore actually beneficial in heart disease.

The Chinese in their ancient medicine administered ground-up "dragons' bones" to children with convulsions. "Dragons' bones" were the bones of dino-

Hammurabi receiving the code from the Sun God.

saurs long exposed to the weather in places like the Gobi Desert. Today in infantile tetany, or convulsions, the physician administers calcium, the main ingredient of bone. Burnt sponge to treat simple goiter was another remedy. It was superstitious, empiric in origin, but its value is now demonstrated in the modern use of iodine for this condition.

These few remedies, however, are great exceptions. The vast number of animal remedies used by early men, and they included almost every conceivable animal product, had no actual beneficial effect; they were mere superstitions. Thus the Egyptians gave a whole skinned mouse for childhood disease; ancient mummies of children are found today with the remains of the mouse still in the stomach. Centuries later at Rome, in the beginning of the Christian era, Pliny advised the same remedy as a preventive against toothache.

It has been said by some authors that the use of animal products by ancient man was the beginning of modern organotherapy. But this is true only in appearance. The early men ate the organs of animals because of a believed mystical virtue; the modern use of such substances as thyroid extract is based upon a sound scientific demonstration of the body's specific need for them. The ancient man eating the raw pancreas of a sacrificed goat in the belief that the Gods would give him good luck and the diabetic of today injecting insulin, a product made from the pancreas, to relieve his disease bear a resemblance that is a mere

A surgical operation as illustrated in a medieval medical text of the twelfth or thirteenth century.

coincidence. The one practice was based upon mysticism, religious beliefs; the other upon sound and demonstrated scientific fact. And few indeed of the ancient remedies have been found to have even a semblance of benefit.

What has been said concerning animal remedies applies likewise to those of vegetable origin. Trees and plants, so early man believed, were the abode of spirits. Eating the plant or drinking its juice brought the virtue of the spirit to the human flesh. Even today among uncivilized races the intoxicating action of alcoholic drinks is attributed to possession by the *spirit* of the vegetable from which the drink is made, and such specific use of the word spirits still survives in our language. Almost literally every plant substance that has grown upon the face of the earth has been used in treating disease. The great majority have no virtue, but the early type of medical practice made no discrimination in such matters, and the old herb remedies, mostly useless, have been carried down even into modern times. Just as in the case of the animal remedies, some few, used first for mystical reasons or perhaps empirically, have been found by modern science to be of outstanding merit.

Along with the plant lore of healing there grew up also the plant lore of poisons. Early men quickly found that some vegetable substances had spirits that were indeed harmful, even deadly to the human being. In his practice of black magic the early medicine man dealt with them, and in the Middle Ages the

A portrayal of the works of Vesalius by Gerard Dou.

compounding of poisons was considered a fine art, encouraged by scheming nobility.

Animals and vegetables were early used in medicine, but mineral substances came later, the majority much later. So we shall reserve the discussion of them until we come to the 15th century of the Christian era and the beginning of the great medical conflict between the Galenists, or herb doctors, and the followers of Paracelsus, the mineral doctors.

Plant and animal remedies and religious ceremony were not the only methods used by the priest-physicians of ancient times, for as we come into Chaldean, Egyptian, and Babylonian civilizations, we find magic, a magic of astrology and numbers and colors, assuming a greater and greater part in medical practice. The roots of astrology are buried in the magic of savage men; the practice took its systematic form at the hands of the early priests of Eastern civilizations. It influenced medical matters for thousands of years afterwards; its remnants exist today in superstitions.

The believed influence of the moon on bodily functions is shown in our word lunatic. But this effect of the moon's rays was only one of many aspects of its presumed influence. Medicines were given or not given according to the state of the moon. The symbolism connected with the moon's periodic birth, growth, decline, and death affected all sorts of human undertakings as well as disease. The sowing of crops, waging war, marrying, bleeding, cupping, administering medicine were only a few of the things which were scheduled according to the phases of the moon. And these ancient beliefs strongly colored the medical practices of as late a period as the 18th century.

The sun and the stars likewise played their part in medical practice, giving us almost innumerable superstitions, many of which persisted for centuries. Physicians of even as recent a time as two or three hundred years ago often made diagnosis by casting the horoscopes of their patients. And until an even more recent period falling stars and comets were believed to be portents of epidemics. Perhaps the ℞ that stands at the top of the physician's prescriptions may even be a remnant of this once widely prevalent astrological belief. According to some scholars it is an abbreviation for *"recipe"*, meaning *take*, but others hold that it is the astrological sign of Jupiter, under whose protection medicine was generally placed. As such it is a written charm or invocation to the Gods to ensure the efficacy of the remedy.

From astrology it is only a step to the magic of numbers. Even today there exist as superstitions the beliefs that were held by ancient man as vital truths in medical matters. Seven, four, and thirteen were particularly potent numbers, so it was thought. A child born in the seventh month of the calendar was supposed, and still is by some people, to have a better chance of living than one born in the eighth month— actual fact to the contrary. Again, there is the belief that every seventh year the individual regenerates the whole body—puts off the old Adam and renews his flesh. And likewise there were the critical days in the course of disease; four, seven, and nine. Numbers also controlled the dose of drugs. Witness the seven pieces of ergot rye that the "wise women" of Europe gave to the child-bearing women—and perhaps, who knows, there is an ancient significance in the common dose of medicine taken "three times a day."

Colors, too, have played a rôle in medicine. History records pink or red medicine for pale people; and for treating anemia red wines were once supposed to be better than white wines on account of the color. Blood, because of its color, was used for anemia—an excellent remedy, so it happened, not because of its redness but because, as we know now, of the iron it contains. But when we come to such beliefs as the one that the red blood of a black fowl will cure rheumatism, shingles, and other and assorted diseases, we get away even from any empirical basis and plunge instead into the true mystery and magic of colors in medicine.

Practically every substance in the world has been used for medical treatment—used in those days when men with magic and mystery groped blindly in their hope of overcoming their misfortunes or warding off disease. The magic of stones, the healing properties of gems, healing wells and springs, the evil eye—those were the kind of matters that had their play

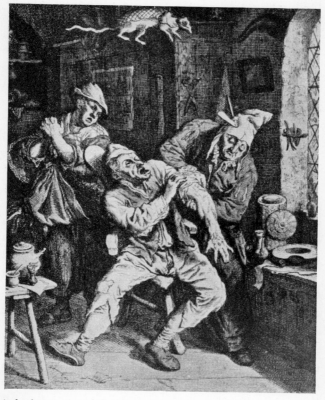

A barber surgeon of the 17th century operating in his shop; the basin on the window seat is held under his "patient's" chin when he performs his duties as a barber.

in medical affairs before science came in to give us the rational basis of modern medicine.

But if we look back to the ancient days of early civilizations, Egyptian, Babylonian, Jewish, we can see rising almost imperceptibly above the morass of mystery and magic the beginning of rational medical practices. There we find some surgery, some well-attested drugs, and, most important of all, the hygiene, the preventive medicine, founded by the ancient Hebrews. But here is a striking fact that shows the earlier stage in the transition of medicine. Although the Jewish people developed a very sound and rational code of hygiene, such was their plane of civilization that, like all medicine of the time, they built this code into their religion. Medicine and religion had not yet separated. Sanitation at their hands became a religious precept; the priests were sanitary police.

Scientific Medicine Is Born—and Dies

IT WAS among the ancient Greeks that the earliest principles of scientific medicine were formulated. And it was among the ancient Greeks that the first complete separation of religion and medicine took place. It was they who first removed mystery from medicine and made it a practice, not of magic, not of religion, but of common sense and observation and logical deduction. This step was perhaps the most important one that has ever occurred in the whole long history of medicine. But it was a step forward in medical progress that was not maintained, for, as we shall see, altho for a brief period the Greeks gave medicine the dignity of a science, it was not held at this level. After the decline of Greece it again sank into the depths of mystery and magic, from which only after the lapse of centuries was it rescued, revived as a science, and finally nurtured into the medicine of today—a medicine which is giving the people of the world the healthiest period that man has ever known.

It is sometimes difficult for us who live in this period to comprehend the extreme hazards of life that existed in bygone days. The medicine of savage peoples did little to prolong life or alleviate suffering other than thru its influence upon the mind. This same statement applies in great measure to the medicine of Grecian days and to that of medieval times. At as late a period as four hundred years ago the average length of life was only eight years; today it is fifty-eight years. Behind those bare figures for the short length of life in bygone days is a tragic story of suffering, sorrow, and untimely death. They were the hazards of life borne in resignation by mankind, from which medical science, particularly in the last seventy-five years, has spared us. One can well give credence to the statement, then, that medical science is the strongest force acting in modern civilization toward human betterment. Modern civilization, as we shall see, is built upon, only made possible by, modern medical science.

Achilles Bandaging Patrokles from a Plaque by Sofias dated about 500 B. C.

And the germ of this science which after centuries was to develop into such a beneficent growth was formed in the days of Grecian civilization—twenty-three hundred years ago. The man who gave us the beginning of science in medicine was a Greek named Hippocrates. Probably no character in all history has thru a single principle exerted so great an influence upon civilization, upon the conditions of humans, as did he whom we revere as the father of modern medicine. Hippocrates separated medicine from mystery and from religion. From his day onward mystery, magic, and medicine cease to be the entire theme of these pages, for he gave us science and medicine.

In the days prior to the work of Hippocrates Grecian medicine was in the hands of a religious organization, the priests of Aesculapius, the deified Grecian hero of medicine. The marble temples dedicated to this God were on the country hillsides, overlooking the blue Aegean. Olive groves and columned porticoes made them beautiful sanatoria. Beyond the entry of each was a statue of Aesculapius, represented as a bearded man of kindly mien holding a staff about which twined a snake—the caduceus, the emblem of the physician even to this day. Beside him were representations of his daughters, Hygieia and Panacea.

The ill applied for admission to these temples. They slept before the statue of the God. In their dreams he and his daughters were supposed to minister with divine healing to the worshippers. The following day the priests would administer such simple medicaments as their knowledge provided, perform crude surgical operations, and prescribe baths and diet. Good and rational medical attention you would say? Seemingly so, but here was its great drawback. These healing priests assumed no responsibility. The Gods, so they said, brought disease; the Gods and only the Gods could relieve it. The priests could intercede for divine aid, but they had no incentive to seek the cause of disease or to search for means for

cure and prevention. Under such a system of medicine no progress could be made; for all its dignified
and beautiful surroundings the ancient Grecian medicine was, in principle at least, no better than that of
early savage men. The will of deified heroes had come
in to replace the malign influences of spirits; but the
change indicated progress of religion, not of medicine.

It was Hippocrates who brought about a drastic
reform in this temple cult of healing, and his great
accomplishment was to relieve the gods of their responsibility for the prevention and the treatment of
disease and to place that responsibility where it belonged—squarely upon the shoulders of man.

Hippocrates separated medicine from religion. And
then for this now for-the-first-time independent field
he supplied a philosophy and an ethics that were
destined to be the great guiding influences of future
medicine. Hippocrates did not create the medical
knowledge of his time; the Egyptians long before
the Greeks had observed symptoms and had found
some practical remedies. The medical knowledge of
isolated facts recorded upon their stone tablets often
seems fully as great as that which Hippocrates possessed. No doubt it was. But here is the great difference. Hippocrates took these isolated facts, this
empirical knowledge, and coördinated it; he made it
into a flexible science. Other men had observed the
symptoms of disease, but it was Hippocrates who first
sat beside his patients and painstakingly sought out
symptoms and recorded them; and these symptoms

were to him not an end in themselves but indications of an underlying condition, a struggle between the patient and the disease which affected him. He took clinical case histories. He founded the bedside method which was to become the distinctive attribute of all great physicians. Having recorded the symptoms of his patients, Hippocrates after wide experience was able to define and classify diseases. Thus he founded the art of diagnosis and prognosis. But throughout all his work his attention was centered upon the patient, not merely upon his symptoms; he dealt with the man as well as with the disease. He kept in his practice the balanced relation between science and art which was to be the distinguishing quality of all great clinicians in all ages.

The descriptions of diseases left by Hippocrates were based on keen and careful observation; they stand today as models of their kind. After his time such accurate observations were not again made in medicine for over eighteen hundred years.

Hippocrates attempted to turn medical thought away from mere speculation toward accurate observation and common sense. He said, "To know is one thing; merely to believe one knows is another. To know is science, but merely to believe one knows is ignorance." It was a difficult path that he pointed out for medicine to follow, one that involved intellectual honesty. Only the highest types of men have the intelligence, the independence, the integrity, and the courage to admit their errors and seek without bias after the truth. Such are they who have given us modern medicine.

But in the years between the days of Hippocrates —the very peak of ancient Grecian culture—and the rise of the modern period, civilization was to decline and with it medicine. Within a century after Hippocrates the decline was already in evidence. Speculation, dogmatization entered the field of medicine to displace observation and clear reasoning. Rival schools sprang into existence; and the men of these schools were more interested in making converts to their dogmas than they were in carrying on unsullied the great principles that Hippocrates had defined.

Three hundred years after Hippocrates, Corinth, the "light of Greece", was destroyed by Roman armies, and Grecian medicine was taken into Rome. At that time the Roman medicine was like that of the Greeks prior to Hippocrates, a matter of the will of the Gods. Grecian medicine displaced the Roman religious medicine, but it was already a deteriorated practice, rapidly losing the impetus given to it by the Father of Medicine.

Once only among the Romans was medicine raised to nearly the dignity that Hippocrates had given it. In the period covered by the century before and the century after the beginning of the Christian Era, medicine made progress in the hands of such men as Celsus, Dioscorides, Aretaeus, and Galen. It is probable that Celsus was not a physician but instead a wealthy patron of science and literature. He com-

Galen, 131–201, as represented in Ambroise Paré's
Surgery.

piled in an encyclopedic manner the medical knowledge of his time. And centuries later in the period of the Renaissance his works were among the first medical books to be printed; they were selected largely because of his elegant literary style.

Dioscorides, a Greek army surgeon in the service of the Emperor Nero, owes his fame to the fact that he originated the *Materia Medica*. During his travels with the army he studied the medicinal herbs of the countries thru which he passed; he described more than 600 plants and plant substances, some 90 of which are still in use today. He recorded as an anesthetic for surgical operations the mandragora wine, which was to become famous in medieval medicine. The *Materia Medica* of Dioscorides was to remain the authoritative work on this subject up to the 17th century.

The next great physician of the Roman period was Aretaeus. Like Hippocrates he was essentially a clinical observer, and it is to him that we owe classical accounts of pneumonia, tetanus, empyema, the aura of epilepsy, and the earliest accurate accounts of insanity.

It was Galen, the last of the great physicians of the Roman period, who was destined for centuries to influence medicine more than any other man. Indeed the period from his time until the 17th century is essentially one of Galenic domination in medicine; the period from the 17th century onward is the revival of Hippocratic medicine.

Galen was unquestionably the most skilled physician of his time, but his lasting fame rests on the fact that he performed experiments to demonstrate the facts of physiology. He essentially formulated the experimental method, which after his time was to lie dormant until the 17th century, when it was revived in the momentous work of Harvey in the demonstration of the circulation of the blood.

Galen was a great physician, but he lacked the intellectual honesty and breadth of vision that Hippocrates had possessed. Hippocrates opened the wide road of medical advancement; Galen closed it, and it remained so closed for nearly 14 centuries. Galen was a theorist; he had an answer for every question, an explanation for every phenomenon. Although his logic was good, his premises were often bad. But it was his logic, his dogmatism, that appealed so strongly to the men of subsequent centuries. His works, rather than those of Hippocrates, were to become the guiding influence, the final authority in all medical matters, until, in fact, it was to become almost a heresy to doubt Galen.

Galen in his therapy inclined strongly to medicaments made up of many vegetable ingredients. His poly-pharmacy in herb doctoring became the much fought over "Galenical system" of the Middle Ages and the Renaissance.

We have mentioned the outstanding men of Roman medicine but not the outstanding contribution of the period: that was sanitation. The Grecian cities were small and remained small because no provision was made for sanitation. In Rome the streets were paved; sewers and aqueducts were built. Clean streets, pure water, and sewage disposal, three of the main assets of public health, had their first practical application. And this practice, which was destined to be revived centuries later and to influence profoundly the 19th and 20th centuries, fell into disuse after the Roman days. Even in Galen's time the empire was declining. Many causes have been given for this decline— social, political, economic—but there was also a medical one, for in these centuries the enervating and deadly malaria had gained a foothold in Italy. Under its influence the people deteriorated. Plagues and pestilences increased in prevalence. Rome fell to the barbarians. But before it fell, medicine had deteriorated; vendors of quack remedies had their shops on the streets; the calling of the physician passed into the hands of professional poisoners, and courtesans who peddled drugs. Medicine ceased to be a science. It again became mystery and magic.

The Contribution of the Orient

AFTER Rome's fall such medical practice as prevailed was essentially in the hands of priests; it was the period of Monastic medicine. For us, in a day when literacy is the common heritage of all civilized men, it is difficult to visualize the social situation that prevailed, to visualize Western Europe with a population in which only the priests could read and write, in which the common man was little better than a slave. It was not that these people had become a degenerated stock; from their progeny centuries later the great medical leaders were to develop and the great scientists who were literally to revolutionize the world in which we live. What was lacking in the Middle Ages was inspiration, the free spirit of aggressive advancement that had given Greece its great intellectual leaders and Rome its martial triumphs.

The Middle Ages represent probably the greatest experimental demonstration of the influence of en-

A page from the works of the Arabic physician Rhazes, fifteenth century

vironment in shaping the characters of men. And this environment was one of submission to recognized authority—unquestioning submission to Church and Feudal Lord preached and exemplified before the child from birth. Potential genius was suppressed or directed into channels barren of practical results.

Now in these years, while the people of Western Europe are living in their walled cities, filthy, undrained, pestilential, while they are suffering from frightful epidemics of disease, while infant mortality rises and length of life declines, let us turn from them to a people of the East who have the liberal aggressive spirit so lacking in the West, a people who are destined to preserve the medical science of the Greeks and Romans.

At the end of the 7th century the Arabs had swept from Arabia thru the Eastern Roman Empire and over Egypt, North Africa, and Spain. The very fate of Western Europe had hung in the balance until the Arabs were defeated in the Battle of Tours in 732. Once settled in their new lands, the Arabs built up their civilization; they turned to cultural pursuits; they were interested in science. They translated the Greek and Roman manuscripts into Arabic, and within two centuries Arabic civilization had developed to a high level.

During the reign of such liberal rulers as Harun al-Rashid of *Arabian Nights* fame, the sciences were patronized extensively. But there were peculiar attributes of the Oriental mind and the Oriental religion which permeated Arabic medicine. And these peculiarities were destined to leave their mark strongly upon the medicine of Europe in subsequent centuries.

The Arabic tendency was toward disputation, hair-splitting disputation. They admired and applauded clever, subtle logic rather than sound and rugged principles. Their way of thinking was as different from that of the Greeks as were the architectures of the two countries—the Grecian columns clear and simple against the sky, the Arabic filigree detailed and intricate.

The theorizing of Galen, his subtle, showy explanations, appealed to the Arabs; the rugged principles of Hippocrates did not. They adapted Galen's theories, his dogmas, and his poly-pharmacy to an Arabic form. Soon at their hands Galen's theories became dogmas; his beliefs took on the forms of axioms as irrefutable as the basic axioms of geometry.

The Arabic knowledge of medicine was to be transplanted into Europe and along with it the peculiar tendencies of Arabic medical thought. And the Europe into which this medicine was to come was one in which, as we have said, authority was accepted without question. Thus the Europeans were to venerate Galen rather than Hippocrates and to accept the works of Galen with an almost religious veneration.

This medicine that is to reach Europe, filtered as it is thru Arabic culture, is a version of Galen flavored strongly by its Arabic contact. A vast amount of stone lore is added; a sturdier fund of pharmacy than Galen's is supplied, an advantage more than counterbalanced by a diminished knowledge of anatomy, for the Arabs made no dissections of the body; some astrology, some mystery, some magic find their places in it; and above and beyond all is an unhealthy tendency to displace the search for truth by the sterile process of disputation.

The Arabic precursors of European medicine were more aggressive clinicians than were their European successors. Great figures stand out among their physicians. There is Rhazes of the 9th and 10th centuries, who described diseases with a fidelity worthy of Hippocrates. He was the first physician to give a clear description of smallpox and measles. And there also a century later was the great Avicenna, whose influence upon European medicine was paramount. His lasting fame rests perhaps upon his production of alcohol and sulphuric acid, the two substances from which, many centuries later, ether was made, one of the great blessings to humanity, as a safe and trustworthy anesthetic. But his immediate fame rested on his books, destined to become the most popular medical literature of Medieval Europe. In spite of his excellent clinical observations his influence was bad. He confirmed in the minds of Europeans, already inclined in that direction, the belief that mental gymnastics, refined argumentation, was more desirable than the drudgery of original investigation. And, perhaps worst of all, he preached the belief that surgery was inferior to medical practice and indeed an entirely separate branch of medicine. When, as late as the time of Frederick the Great, the Prussian Army surgeons as part of their duty shaved the officers of the army, they owed this mark of their degradation to the day when Avicenna cast surgery into disrepute.

It was this great Arab who advanced the doctrine that cautery should be used instead of the knife and thus added cruelty to a practice already horribly cruel—surgery without anesthesia. In justice it must be admitted, though, that the use of the cautery and of boiling oil in treating wounds had one advantage: it helped to control infection in an age when antiseptics were unknown. When some five centuries later the great French surgeon, Ambroise Paré, discarded these practices of Avicenna, there can be little question that infection increased in prevalence. Three hundred years more were to pass before Joseph Lister made his announcement of the antiseptic principle.

We have dwelt to greater length on Arabic medicine than it of itself deserves here—save for one fact. Unlike the practices of China or India or Japan this Arabic medicine is to have a profound influence upon the medicine from which our own of today has developed. So we shall turn now from Arabic medicine already in its zenith, soon to be stationary and then decadent, to Europe of the 11th and 12th centuries. These are the years when Arabic influence is first felt,

radiating from Europe's one medical school, that of
Salerno, a small seashore town near Naples. Here
under Arabic influence medicine is taught for the
first time in the medieval period as a separate branch
of science, in distinction to the Monastic medicine
prevalent elsewhere.

But the Salernian School was not to be the guiding
influence of European medicine; it was a feeble, very
feeble, light in a great wilderness. It is best remembered by its famous medical poem said to have been
prepared for Robert Duke of Normandy, son of
William the Conqueror, the *Regimen Salernitanum,*
essentially a compendium of practical advice replete
with jingling lines such as '"Joy, temperance, and
repose slam the door on the doctor's nose." After the
invention of printing it went thru some 240 editions,
and portions of it were translated into English at
the time of Queen Elizabeth under the title *The
Englishman's Doctor*. The translator was the famous
Sir John Harington, inventor of the water-closet.

The outstanding medical contribution of the
School of Salerno was the writings of Roger of
Palermo. He prescribed burnt sponge for goiter, used
mercury salves for skin diseases, and sutured the
intestine over a tube, but he preached the healing of
wounds by second intention in the Galenic belief that
pus formation was a necessary and desirable part of
the reparative process. This problem of wound healing is to occupy much attention during the period
extending from these years to the 19th century and

Page from the Canon of Avicenna, *fifteenth century edition.*

the time of Lister. In all these years only three men
before Lister upheld the doctrine that wounds should
be so treated that pus did not form. Two of them
came in this Medieval period—Theodoric, Bishop of
Cervia, and Henri de Mondeville. The third was the
great Swiss of the early Renaissance—Paracelsus.

We now come to the thirteenth and fourteenth
centuries—a period characterized for our story by
the Crusades to the Orient, the rise of universities,
and epidemics of the Black Death. These epidemics,
which wiped out nearly half of the sparse population
of Europe, were followed by that amazing hysterical
outburst, the dancing mania. At that time the population of Western Europe was less than that of the
British Isles alone today.

The rise of medical schools, especially at Naples,
Palermo, and Montpellier, impinged upon Salerno so
that it was destined to lead but a feeble existence
until 1811, when it was abolished by Napoleon.

The Crusades were avenues thru which Arabic
medicine was brought in its full force into Europe.
And as we have said, it was a Europe peculiarly re-
ceptive to this dogmatized version of Galen. The
Arabic medicine was accepted and venerated; it furnished endless material for sterile argument but no
inspiration for progress. If we seek thru these years
for men who advanced medicine, our search is nearly
fruitless. Two only, and they surgeons, stand out.
One is the Henri de Mondeville of the 13th century
whom we have mentioned as a supporter of the

Hippocratic belief that wounds should be kept clean and allowed to heal free from pus if possible. His influence was not great. The other was Guy de Chauliac, a man of rare talents and noble character, who by his example helped to elevate surgery to a more dignified position, who believed—a revolutionary concept in those days—that a knowledge of anatomy was essential to surgery. But Guy de Chauliac, in direct opposition to Theodoric and Mondeville, advocated the meddlesome treatment of wounds and the application of salves and plasters. His influence was so strong that his beliefs retarded the progress of surgery for some six centuries.

Of medical progress in Europe there is little to record until the 16th century. The intervening years were years of sterile disputations. Galenic—Arabic Galenic—medicine had taken its hold upon the medical profession and the clergy with nearly the strength of the precepts of the Bible and in an age when it was heresy to doubt the Bible.

To find any notable progress arising from medicine in these years we must turn to one branch of it—pharmacy—and to a progress that is essentially social rather than medical—one of enormous benefit to mankind. For the pharmaceutical beliefs of the times led to exploration; and the exploration resulted in great geographical discoveries—including that of America.

Here again we find the Arabic influence. The pharmacy of the East employed the herbs and plant products native to the Orient—aloes, benzoin, camphor, cinnamon, cloves, cubebs, ginger, musk, opium, pepper, and rhubarb. In adopting Arabic medicine the physicians of Europe likewise adopted the products of Arabic pharmacy. A brisk trade resulted in what today we should call mainly spices, but which in those days were highly desirable medicaments. The caravan routes of trade were slow and expensive, and so explorers set out in ships to find a shorter route for the spice trade. Vasco da Gama sailed round Cape Horn; Columbus sailed to America, believing he had reached India. And for centuries afterwards the seaboard countries of Europe strove for the supremacy of the spice traffic, the lightest and most lucrative cargo a ship could carry, for in those days products common to our kitchens as well as the shelves of our pharmacists commanded enormous prices.

The struggle for the spice trade was a struggle for naval supremacy. In turn Venice, then Portugal, then Holland, and finally England became mistress of the seas, and each in turn so rose as a by-product of pharmacy. But since their naval achievements were only by-products, we must leave their story to the general historian and return to our original subject: mystery, magic, and medicine.

Leaders of Revolt: Paracelsus, Vesalius, Paré

As WE have said, the Middle Ages failed of progress because there was lacking the spark of inspiration,

Thomas Linacre, 1460–1524, one of the medical humanists of the Renaissance; he has been called the "restorer of learning" in England.

The famous Paracelsus 1493–1541.

the leadership of broadminded, clear-thinking men, untrammeled by tradition. A vast amount of energy was wasted in disputes that were sterile from their inception. The learned men of a medical school might debate the question as to whether Eve had a navel, since she was not born of woman. But such impracticalities healed no wounds, stopped no epidemics, and brought no ease to the suffering. Something was needed to free men from the ban of absolute authority and restore liberty of thought.

The use of gunpowder and the invention of printing were two of the most potent liberating forces. Gunpowder ended feudalism; printing opened the way for self-education.

And in these years which are called the Renaissance, the period from 1453 to 1600, free thought returned in a measure, and with it came a spirit of criticism, dissatisfaction with prevailing conditions. Stultifying faith in tradition and supine dependence upon authority gave way gradually to skepticism and independence.

The Renaissance may be said to begin the year that Constantinople fell; a year before this date Leonardo da Vinci was born, and a year after it the Gutenberg Bible was printed—notable events. With the fall of Constantinople the scholars of that city came as refugees into Italy. They exerted a marked influence upon European culture, for they brought with them the philosophies of Plato and the teachings of Hippocrates, a better pabulum for the growth of independence in a country hungry for knowledge than the desiccated diet of Aristotle and Galen which had been spread before the scholars.

In our story here we have been able to mention only three or four men who in Europe contributed to medical progress during the 700 years that preceded the Renaissance. But now, stirred by the new-found freedom, men are turning with faltering, uncertain steps, with limbs stiff from disease, to the practice and principle after the example of Hippocrates. In these years the first step toward modern medicine can be discerned—a movement that gains with accelerating impetus to reach our own times and give us during the last seventy-five years the greatest and the most beneficent measures that any science has ever bestowed upon mankind. And with this acceleration come in a rapid succession men, leaders, whose work has shaped the medicine of our day.

The three great medical leaders of the Renaissance were Paracelsus, Vesalius, and Paré. But there were many others and lesser men who contributed to the progress of medicine. Early in the Renaissance Thomas Linacre, physician to Henry VII and Henry VIII, called in England the "Restorer of Learning", translated accurately the original works of Galen, thus breaking thru the Arabic tradition and restoring medicine a step nearer to Hippocrates. Next came François Rabelais, who, in our interest in his broad satires of social conditions, *Gargantua* and *Pantagruel*, we often forget was the physician who first translated the aphorisms of Hippocrates. And there was Eucharius Röslin, who wrote a book on obstetrics called the *Rosengarten,* a very feeble venture, but the only book of its kind in Europe for fourteen centuries and one extensively plagiarized during the following century. Its importance lies in the fact that he obtained his information from the works of Soranus of Ephesus, who lived in the 2nd century. Most of the obstetrical innovations of the Renaissance, and of the 17th century as well, date back to this same Soranus. In fact all the medical progress of the early years of the Renaissance was in the nature of a revival, a progress which was to lift medicine toward the level which it had achieved in ancient Greece.

This revival was first a task of translation and publication at the hands of the medical humanists such as Linacre and Rabelais and Röslin. Thru their efforts the way was made ready for the aggressive liberal thinkers who were to go beyond mere book knowledge and strike out vigorously for the privilege of medical progress. And certainly that is precisely what Paracelsus did. He struck out with a bullying aggression, as if medical progress were to be settled like a brawl in the tap-room of a tavern. While the efforts of the humanists might in time have worn down traditions, Paracelsus shattered them.

He was a Swiss, a queer mixture of a man, of keenest intellect and coarsest fiber, an unusual combination. Like most students of these times he led a wandering life. That was the only way anyone could

*Ambroise Paré, 1510–1590, the father of French
surgery.*

keep in touch with what was going on; there were no scientific periodicals, no newspapers, and where a postal service existed, it was uncertain and expensive. Consequently most of the university students, the professors as well, and many physicians wandered from one university to another. Most of these itinerant students were true vagabonds, begging and stealing for their livelihood.

Paracelsus in his travels, so Garrison says, collected information from every source, "and by his relations with barbers, executioners, bath keepers, gypsies, midwives, and fortune tellers, he learned a great deal about medical practice, and incidentally acquired an unusual knowledge of folk-medicine and a permanent taste for low company." But Paracelsus was a keen and educated man; he was able to discard most of the superstitions that surrounded the medicine of barbers and executioners and old women, and to uncover the kernel of practical value that it contained. Nevertheless he was a product of the times, and his writings in places are so shrouded in a sort of quasi-mysticism as to render them almost unintelligible.

Paracelsus, perhaps because of his intimate contact with the people, discarded the Latin at that time required as the language of all scholars; he taught in the vernacular—a startling innovation. And what was even worse, from the point of view of the times, he taught from his own vivid experiences and common sense rather than from the dead pages of Galen and Avicenna. In fact, when for a year he

Medicine à la mode *settles the controversy between the supporters of herb therapy and the supporters of mineral therapy by riding over both of them.*

taught at Basel—a year later he left the city hastily, —he opened his lectures by making a public bonfire of the works of Galen and Avicenna. Then he harangued the students in the popular language and attempted to implant in them a reverence for the principles of Hippocrates.

But his greatest blow to the Galenic system was his introduction of mineral medicaments. With a reckless disregard of the death that might be dealt out for such heresy, he discarded the feeble herb medicines of Galen and substituted such strong mineral medicaments as mercury, lead, sulphur, iron, and arsenic. In short he founded the chemical school and precipitated a controversy that was to last for three centuries. The adherents of Galen maintained that the Galenicals were the only safe medicaments; the

followers of Paracelsus supported the powerful mineral substances. And both in a way were right. The
Galenicals were mainly harmless; they were also
mainly useless. The minerals were in some instances
decidedly beneficial, but they were also, in the large
doses given in bygone days, often harmful.

The medical knowledge of Paracelsus was sound
and practical—we have already mentioned that in the
long period between the time of Theodoric and
Mondeville and that of Lister he was the only supporter of the principle of keeping wounds clean. But
the greatest contribution of Paracelsus was one that
emanated from his own enormously strong personality. Everywhere in his travels, in his writings as
well, he preached revolt—revolt against dogma—and
the return to the Hippocratic principle. He struck
boldly and belligerently for the right of individual
judgment. His actions, his words, were bold, for his
was a day when to stray from the beaten path of
authorized knowledge was heresy for which the in-
novator might be burned at the stake.

Galileo was forced to recant, you remember, when
he said the earth revolved about the sun. Michael
Servetus, who came so near to anticipating Harvey
in discovering the circulation of the blood, was
burned to death at the order of Calvin for a mere
theological quibble. Paracelsus escaped such penalties,
and his bold example started men to thinking independently in regard to medical problems. Out of
this new-found independence, timidly followed at

Title page from the Anatomy of Andreas Vesalius.

first, came the revival of the scientific spirit, a re-
newed search for facts. And one of the first fruits
of this movement was the search for the facts of
anatomy.

It seems almost incredible that even at this late
date, the 16th century, the true anatomy of the body
was not accurately known. Galen had described it,
but he based his facts upon dissection of hogs and
apes. The Arabs had almost ignored anatomy. One
has only to turn to medical manuscripts dating back
in the 15th century or even to the pictures, so
common, of the death dance, showing skeletons, to
see lack of anatomical knowledge of any structure
beneath the skin. These old anatomical drawings bear
about the same relation to the true structure of the
body as the formalized Egyptian hieroglyphics do to
the figures they portray. It was Andreas Vesalius, a
man of German extraction, a teacher at Padua, who
was the first true anatomist.

Vesalius was by no means the first physician to dissect the body, but he was the first to dissect it un-
blinded by the authority of Galen. He recorded what
he saw and not what authority said he should see. The
fruit of his work is the great *De Fabrica Humani
Corporis,* published in 1543. In one sweep he dis-
cards the Galenic tradition and restores to the human
body the structure with which it is properly endowed.
No longer does man have forced upon him the muscles
of the dog and the monkey, the pelvis of an ox, and
a five-lobed liver; womankind in addition is spared

Michael Servetus, 1509–1553; he came close to the discovery of the circulation of the blood; he was burned to death by order of Calvin for a theological quibble.

the two-horned uterus of the brutes. Vesalius goes even further and attacks the popular anatomical superstitions of his time—the indestructible bone of Luz from which the body was supposed to be resurrected and the famous missing rib of Adam.

There are deficiencies in Vesalius as from our own time we view his work—he believed that the nasal secretion came from the brain, a fact disproved a hundred years later, and thus he gave support to the practice of taking snuffs to "purge the brains." But in the days in which he wrote, the work of Vesalius was revolutionary. The response was immediate and violent. He escaped the fate of Servetus, for the condemnation came not from the clergy but from the men of his own profession. By some he was tolerantly ignored as tho he were a naughty child, others openly derided him, and some there were who used the authorities to impose upon him petty persecutions. In indignation Vesalius, then barely thirty, burned his manuscripts, retired from anatomy, and became physician to Emperor Charles V.

During his retirement the storm he had aroused quieted down. His pupil Fallopius, famous for the discovery of the Fallopian tube, went on with the great work; Eustachius compiled his dissections—they remained unprinted in the Papal Library for 162 years—and Sylvius named structure after structure in the body. The anatomy that Vesalius had founded was being accepted, but Vesalius, in retirement, was being forgotten. Finally in 1563 he went on a pilgrimage to Jerusalem, although no one knows why he went, many have speculated, and the best speculation seems to be the most prosaic one, that he was bored with court life. On his way back he received word that he was to have back his old position at Padua. But he was never to realize the ambition that had cankered him so since the day he had become a courtier. On the journey home he sickened and died.

Vesalius's work had a profound influence upon

A room in the Hôtel Dieu of Paris, 16th century wood cut.

medical progress, and the most immediate effect, as would be expected, was upon surgical practice. And here then we come to the third of the great leaders of Renaissance medicine—Paracelsus, Vesalius, and Paré.

Strikingly different personalities were these men: Paracelsus crude, forceful, domineering, sweeping in the breadth of his conclusions; Vesalius dignified, straightforward, suave, but hot tempered, painstakingly thorough in his work; and Ambroise Paré, filled with ripe common sense, possessed of a keen sense of humor, equally at home in the crude army camps and at the court in a period when intrigue ruled, the court dominated by Catherine de Medici. Paré was the least strong of the three great medical personalities of the

Renaissance, but he was the most lovable, the most human of them. Read by all means his *Surgery,* the garrulous and gossipy account of his adventures at war.

There he tells how as a boy of 19, a rustic barber's apprentice, he came to Paris in 1529. Three years' training in the Hôtel Dieu, and Paré was an army surgeon under Anne de Montmorency, a green army surgeon uninured to the horrors of war. He tells how shocked he was when he found in a barn three men wounded hopelessly, and he says, "Beholding them with pity, there came an old soldier who asked me if there was any way of curing them. I told him no. At once he approached them and cut their throats gently and without anger. Seeing this great cruelty, I said to him that he was an evil man. He answered me that he prayed God that when he should be in such a case, he might find some one who would do the same for him." Such was the school in which Paré had his apprenticeship.

He tells too how almost by accident—and yet one must suspect that his kindliness dictated it equally— he first broke thru the horribly cruel tradition promulgated by the Arabs that "diseases not curable by iron are curable by fire." He, as an army surgeon, was expected by tradition to pour into gunshot wounds boiling oil and to cauterize amputations to control hemorrhage. Paré, running short of oil—so he says—tried letting wounds alone. They healed better. For stopping hemorrhage he used the ligature to tie off blood vessels, a practice that had fallen into disuse since the time of Celsus. Paré's whole beneficent philosophy is summed up in that phrase he used so often, one connected inseparably with him: "I dressed his wounds; God healed him."

Paré raised surgery to a dignity that made a tolerable situation for the men who did actual surgical practice. In those days there were two kinds of surgeons: surgeons of the long robe, erudite dignitaries who offered opinions and prescribed plasters, and the barber-surgeons, or surgeons of the short robe, of whom Paré was one, men who performed actual surgical operations but who were at the beck and call of their superiors, the surgeons of the long robe. Paré broke thru this sterile etiquette. He wrote in the vernacular; he defied the long-robe gentry and succeeded in some measure in bringing surgery into the hands of the men who did surgery.

A great many of the surgical practices in use today date back to Paré. The ligature we have mentioned; he used podalic version in obstetrics, introduced artificial eyes, massage, and the truss in hernia; he greatly improved artificial limbs and the operation for hernia. But it was his keen common sense that supplied the great impetus to the surgery of the time— he made surgery a practical art. And his surgery carried on supreme for nearly 200 years, until John Hunter made surgery a science.

Before turning from the three great leaders of the Renaissance there is at least one other man whom we must include here, Girolamo Fracastoro, physician, poet, geologist, and astronomer. His greatest fame rests on a poem, *Syphilidis, sive Morbi Gallici*, published in 1530. The malady spreading over Europe in this period and not yet well understood was called by many names; it was Fracastoro who coined for it the name syphilis. His poem is a summary of the prevailing knowledge of the disease.

In considering only such men as Paracelsus, Vesalius, and Paré one obtains a false impression of the virtues of Renaissance medicine; these men stood almost alone. They are not representative of the medicine of the time. The practice by and large was in the hands of those whose medical knowledge was little if any better than that of the rude empirics of the Middle Ages. Even the wealthy were treated by physicians who made diagnoses by inspection of urine, by astrological observations, or by palmistry, and who prescribed according to ritual and placed great hope in amulets and charms. Surgery was largely in the hands of barbers and executioners or in those of mountebanks and vagabonds who moved from town to town to escape the consequences of their acts.

Science Becomes a Fad

LEAVING now the Renaissance, we pass into the 17th century. The two are different in this respect: in the Renaissance scientific investigation was a rare novelty undertaken by a few outstanding men; in the 17th

Girolamo Fracastoro, 1484–1553. He is famous for his poem,
Syphilidis, sive Morbi Gallici, *published in Venice, 1530, from*
which the disease syphilis derives its name.

century science, or what was called science, has become a fad, patronized and dabbled in by a host of
men. Many individual workers, for there is yet no
organized effort to a defined progress, make their re-
spective contributions, each according to the personal
conceptions and ability of the man. There results a
vast amount of absurd pseudo-science and along with
it some of the most important contributions to real
science. Thus in the same century, in the same court,
Harvey makes his momentous discoveries regarding

the circulation of the blood and Sir Kenelm Digby obtains the support of the King for his absurd powder of sympathy which is supposed to heal wounds when bloody garments are merely dipped into a solution of it. Shakespeare and Milton, Rembrandt and Velasquez, make their contributions to literature and art; Newton, Kepler, Galileo change the whole conception of the solar system; and while the progress goes on, the Kings of France and England continue to carry out the superstitious ritual of touching scrofulous patients to heal them—the Royal Touch for the King's Evil—and epidemics are attributed to the appearance of comets. Extreme bleeding is the therapeutic forte of most physicians; the materia medica is encumbered by a vast number of vile and useless remedies which have no basis except that of superstition. The 17th century is a hodgepodge of modern realism and childish credulity. Medicine, revived, is just passing from childhood to adolescence.

The great discoveries of the 17th century in the practical care of the patients of that period are of little importance. It is later, much later, that they are to become the basis of the beneficent measures of modern medicine. Overshadowing all others is William Harvey's discovery of the circulation. But the actual discovery of the course of blood flow is far less important than the method by which he arrived at his conclusions. He applied measurements, mathematical measurements, to vital phenomena; and was the first man so to do.

Touchpiece for the King's Evil, a gold coin presented to the sufferers from scrofula when touched for this disease by the English royalty.

The Manner of His Majesties Curing the Disease,
CALLED THE
KINGS-EVIL.

Portion of a broadside announcing the ceremony of the touch for the King's Evil.

67

The knowledge of vital action that we have today, that makes modern medicine practical, is based on similar measurements. To know that the human body is warm, to know that the blood in the arteries has pressure, to know that a man breathes air are general facts, known for centuries, and they gain practical importance in medicine only when measurements are applied to them. It is the answers to the questions what temperature, what pressure, what volume, that give modern medicine its precision and its claim to being a science. Harvey was a modern scientist.

The man himself was short and slight, black haired, red faced, quick in action, and so, we are told, not by any means the best practitioner of his time.

It was in 1628 that he published his great book *De Motu Cordis*. Sixteen-twenty-eight may seem like a long time ago, but in the light of historical sequence it is very recent. The *Mayflower* had landed at Plymouth only eight years before that date; and seven years after it Harvard College was opened. The men who taught the first classes in Harvard could have known Shakespeare personally; the professor of medicine—if there had been one at Harvard then— could have known Harvey. But Shakespeare and Harvey were studied neither in this university nor in those in Europe. The ancient philosophers still held sway, and what they taught about the blood flow was this: the liver was the center of the blood system. Food was elaborated into a something called "natural spirits" and brought to the liver. From this center

William Harvey, 1578–1657; he demonstrated the circulation of the blood.

the blood ebbed out gradually, like a tide, reaching every part of the body. In the brain the "natural spirits" were changed into "animal spirits" and ran out along the nerves, emptying from their tips back into the veins. These ancients knew that the heart beat and that the arteries expanded; but they made no measurements. They guessed badly, for they thought that the heart and the arteries expanded at the same time. The heart, they believed, warmed the blood; the lungs fanned and cooled it. This conception, a fine bit of "armchair philosophy", was not a very substantial basis upon which to study and treat diseases of the heart.

What Harvey did was to put this conception to experimental proof. The first thing he discovered was that the heart, instead of expanding when the beat was felt against the ribs, was really contracting, pushing blood into the arteries. Then he wanted to know if, when the heart expanded, the blood ran back in the arteries and into the heart. He tied a cord about the forearm of a man; when he squeezed it just tight enough to shut off the veins, the arteries kept bringing blood until the veins below the band were distended and the arm swollen. The veins above the band were collapsed. Obviously the blood flowed away from the heart in the arteries and reached the veins. Now, reasoned Harvey, if the blood kept flowing out from the heart it would all be gone in a short time. He made measurements to estimate the quantity of blood in the body and found that there was not enough for the heart to pump very long unless the supply were replenished. The obvious conclusion was, of course, that the blood flowed back to the heart in the veins. And step by step he proved this point.

How much simpler was Harvey's way than that of the theorists. And yet such were the times that these theorists held sway. Harvey, like Vesalius, was abused for daring to doubt Galen. But it was characteristic also of these more advanced times that the opposition soon died out, and men began to find added proofs

Athanasius Kircher, 1602–1680; he advanced a theory of parasitic origin of infection two hundred years before Pasteur and Koch demonstrated the rôle that bacteria play in infection.

to support Harvey's discovery. And what is more important, they adopted his method of using measurements to find the answers to other physiological problems.

Harvey's work centered attention particularly upon two functions of the body, the circulation itself and respiration, for when he disproved the ancient beliefs concerning the action of the heart, he disproved simultaneously the beliefs concerning the function of the lungs.

Harvey could only speculate as to how the blood

went from the arteries to the veins, for no one at that time had seen the capillaries. But that mystery was soon to be cleared up, for there was just coming into use an instrument destined to be one of the most valuable in all medical discovery—the microscope.

Perhaps the first man to use this new instrument, then of very feeble magnifying powers, in studying disease was a Jesuit priest named Athanasius Kircher. Besides being a physician he was one of the first students of Egyptian hieroglyphics. He invented the ear trumpet; he enunciated clearly, though centuries ahead of his time, the belief that infectious diseases were caused by living parasites. He sought for them with his microscope in victims of the plague and believed he had found them, but what he saw were unquestionably red blood-corpuscles. Before the microscope supplied the answer of how the blood flowed from arteries to veins, it passed thru the hands of many men. There was Robert Hooke, whose book, *Micrographia,* so fascinated Pepys. It was Hooke who first recorded the cellular structure of plants. Then came Jan Swammerdam, who described the red corpuscles. Next appeared that amazing character, Anton van Leeuwenhoek of Delft, interested in microscopy as a hobby—he by trade a draper and the janitor of the city hall—who fairly showered the learned societies with his discoveries. But they were not systematic studies; they were observations of a man who put under his microscope everything he could lay his hands upon. And the one of greatest importance, like most of the important discoveries of the 17th century, was of no practical benefit at the time but only some centuries later—he saw protozoa and he pictured bacteria in their true form.

The greatest microscopist of these pioneer days was the Italian, Marcello Malpighi. He founded histology as a science. And it was he who brought the final step in Harvey's demonstration of the circulation. He saw the capillaries. He demonstrated the essential vascular structure of the lungs and showed the minute structure of the air sacs.

Turning now from the new fields opened up by the microscope, we come to the other aspect of Harvey's discovery—that concerning the function of the lungs. If breathing did not cool the blood, what did it do? That was the question—why did men breathe? It was a question that was not to be answered for another hundred years. But the beginnings were made in the 17th century. Harvey had noted that the blood changed color in the lungs. It was John Mayow who demonstrated that this change of color is due to exposure to air, that the blood takes up some constituent of the air. So close did Mayow come to the discovery of oxygen.

Our discussion here of medical progress in the 17th century has centered around Harvey—Harvey and the microscope. We have said little of practical treatment in the field of surgery and medicine. With one exception—and that is Sydenham—there is little to

John Banister delivering a lecture on anatomy at the Barber-Surgeons Hall in London, 1581. The red and white barber's pole is in evidence.

be said. The medicine and surgery in practice in the 17th century were essentially the medicine and surgery of the 16th century.

True Germany had its Paré in the surgeon Wilhelm Fabry, "father of German surgery." True also that one of the most valuable drugs in the materia medica was introduced in this century—quinine, made from cinchona bark from South America. But if you wish to see medicine as it was in the hands of the average practitioner, read Molière's satires.

Yet there was one man whom such satire did not and could not portray—the serious Sydenham of England, called the English Hippocrates. Here was a man who was left unmoved by the brilliant work of Harvey, by the discoveries of Malpighi and Mayow. He did not believe in experiments; he did not believe in theories. He believed only in observation and experience. He was a practical practitioner. And this we say here in praise, for in the medical progress made so far not enough facts had been discovered upon which to formulate practical theories. And already in his time men were showing the tendencies to those speculations which were to render the medicine of the 18th century far from practical.

The fame of Sydenham rests upon his common sense and keen observation. He described disease with the fidelity of Hippocrates. Gout, scarlatina (he named the disease and differentiated it from measles), malaria, dysentery, cholera—of them he left descriptions that were masterpieces. His treatment was simple and effective: cinchona for intermittent fevers, iron for anaemia, cooling drinks in fever. For a hundred years and more his clear, simple, practical measures offered by far the best that medicine could offer—seldom attained and never exceeded.

A Century of Transition

SYDENHAM, as we have said, ignored the scientific investigations of his century. The fact is that not enough discoveries had been made to supply a practical basis for medical advancement. The discoveries were scattered. Harvey defined the circulation, but the facts he disclosed, fundamental as they were, did not greatly aid the practicing physician. No system in the body stands alone. The principles of cardiac action are intimately associated with the principle of energetics, of respiration, of digestion, of muscular action, of nervous control. Knowledge of these things was yet to come. And so also was that of pathology. Another century and more was to pass before enough facts had been accumulated to furnish a basis for scientific medicine.

The 18th century, into which we now pass, was not one of great scientific discovery so far as medicine was concerned; it was one of systematization, with insufficient material at hand for the formation of good systems. Such was not the case in mathematics and physics, for these sciences yielded valuable results under this essentially speculative approach.

The attitude of the 18th century mind was in the nature of a reaction. In the 17th century there was an enthusiastic but diffuse interest in all matters scientific and pseudo-scientific; the interest was largely naïve and uncritical. In the 18th century a critical attitude had developed, one of sophistication. Men were taking stock of the accumulated facts, correlating them, seeking principles. However great the advantages of this critical scrutiny in the field of the mathematical sciences, little benefit accrued to medicine at that time. There is little of the rugged work such as that represented in the discoveries of Harvey, Malpighi, and Leeuwenhoek.

In this 18th century men were philosophizing: Kant and Leibnitz led in Germany's great cultural ascendency; while in France Voltaire preached skepticism and Rousseau the equality of men. But when philosophy is applied to medicine in the stage of development to which it had then attained, there appear not valid advances but instead such excrescences as the plausible absurdity of John Brown, who launched the Brunonian system, which attracted a vast amount of attention.

Under this system all diseases fall into one or another of two simple categories: those in which there is too much bodily excitement or those in which there is too little. Opium and alcohol respectively, according to Brown, correct the two conditions. He died of abuse of the two therapeutic agents he advocated.

At the complete extreme from Brown was the great systematist, Albrecht von Haller of Bern and Göttingen. Haller was a brilliant, indefatigable worker, interested and active in the literature of every phase of medicine and taking occasional excursions into poetry and historical novels as well. But like so many men of superabundant energy (he wrote some 13,000 scientific papers) and diffuse interests, his work, altho not superficial by any means, is not deep and fundamental. He systematized the known facts, wrote in an encyclopaedic fashion, and theorized, and theorized quite soundly.

The greatest clinician of the 18th century was

unquestionably Herman Boerhaave of Leyden. His reputation as a consultant extended throughout the world, but it is doubtful if he advanced medical progress. His methods of treatment were essentially those of Sydenham; Boerhaave was a better teacher, but he lacked Sydenham's capacity for describing diseases.

As we have said, the fundamental scientific advancement of the 18th century was in the field of chemistry, physics, and invention, rather than in medicine. What a galaxy of famous names is associated with these sciences: Lagrange, Cavendish, Laplace, Scheele, Lavoisier, Galvani, Volta, Watt, Fulton, Stephenson, Fahrenheit, and Franklin. But the fundamental science that these men established had yet no place in medicine; a century—nearly two centuries were to elapse before chemistry, mathematics, and physics were to be applied, as at the hands of Harvey, to the quantitative study of physiological phenomena.

To stand with these great names of science, medicine of the 18th century has to offer only two, John Hunter and Edward Jenner; and let us add here as lesser luminaries the names of Giovanni Morgagni, Stephen Hales, William Smellie, and Leopold Auenbrugger. Morgagni at Padua was the first man to systematically correlate disease conditions in the body with the clinical symptoms arising from them. Essentially he founded pathological anatomy, but his work did not influence the medicine of his time.

Leopold Auenbrugger, 1722–1809; he founded the science of percussion.

Stephen Hales was a cleric with an experimental turn of mind, who first measured the arterial pressure by using his horse as a subject. William Smellie computed the first correct obstetrical measurements of the pelvis. To Leopold Auenbrugger we owe the art of percussion. It is characteristic of the century that Morgagni's studies, Hales' discovery, Smellie's observations, were not incorporated into medical practice and that Auenbrugger's method lay neglected for thirty years, until in the next century Corvisart took it up and popularized it. We look back at these men as great pioneers, but we evaluate

79

their work in the light of subsequent achievement rather than by their effect upon the medicine of the time.

The same is true of the achievements of Lavoisier, the great French scientist who supplied the answer to the question which had so puzzled Harvey—why we breathe. He showed that the oxygen of the air, discovered by Mayow and Priestley and Scheele, is taken into the body and used to burn food, and that this combustion is an essential phenomenon of life. Lavoisier's head fell under the guillotine in the revolution in 1794. His astounding discovery, so fundamental to subsequent medical advancement, led at the time only to medical fads of treatment and to a wholly erroneous conception of the effects of carbon dioxide in the vitiation of air in poorly ventilated rooms.

Hunter and Jenner remain as the men who in the 18th century influenced most profoundly the medical progress of their day. John Hunter made a science of surgery. Up to his time all surgical practices were essentially such as Paré had used. Surgery was a form of treatment only and as such subordinate to clinical medicine. A leg obviously gangrened or seriously injured was to be amputated; the surgeon amputated it, with such knowledge of anatomy and skill as he might possess. That situation sums up the surgery of the time when the surgeon was a technician only. John Hunter, on the contrary, provided for surgery more than a basis of

Antoine Laurent Lavoisier, 1743–1794; the physiology of respiration dates from his work.

Stephen Hales, 1677–1761; he made the first observations on the pressure of the blood in the arteries.

anatomy and technique; he correlated surgical procedures with the physiology and pathology of the diseased part. He founded experimental and surgical pathology. He did more perhaps than any other single man to raise surgery (and the surgeon) from a subordinate position to one on a par with clinical medicine.

There was one aspect of Hunterian surgery, however, that for all its advancement in other respects remained the same as that of Paré and of his predecessors. His surgery was still limited to the surface and to the extremities. Hunter did not operate in the abdomen, and few men indeed did so until the advent of antisepsis at the hands of Lister. Injuries, amputations, surface tumors, and especially aneurism (a sequel to the spread of syphilis and the then incomplete methods of cure) occupied the attention of the surgeons.

In personality John Hunter was a sort of rough and ready type, in great contrast to his brother William, a fastidious gentleman who taught anatomy and surgery in London. It was the latter who took his roisterous, uncouth younger brother John in hand and gave him an education. But John, altho the importance of his work far overshadows that of William, never attained the refinement of his brother.

The other great figure in 18th century medicine, Edward Jenner, offers in turn another extreme contrast of personality to that of John Hunter. Jenner was a quiet, friendly man, a country practitioner of Gloucestershire. He lived simply, wrote poems of some merit, and played on the flute and violin. And this gentle, kindly man was one of the supreme benefactors of all times. Literally he founded preventive medicine and gave us certainly the most valuable of all prophylactic measures—vaccination against smallpox.

Again, as in the case of Harvey, Jenner's work has an importance aside from its direct practical usefulness. Harvey applied mathematics to physiological problems; Jenner made a pure application of the control experiment. Both these endeavors foreshadow the enormous advance of scientific medicine to be made on these fundamental principles.

Jenner was not the first to use prophylactic methods to prevent smallpox. Inoculation, direct transmission of the disease in mild form by means of the pus from smallpox sores, had been in practice in the Orient for a long time. The practice was introduced into England early in the 18th century thru a communication in the *Proceedings of the Royal Society*, and popularized a few years later by Lady Mary Wortley Montagu. In America the practice owed its introduction to Cotton Mather, of the Salem witchcraft episode. The great disadvantage of inoculation lay in the mortality of the method —perhaps three per cent—and in the likelihood that the patients inoculated would become centers from which a virulent smallpox might be spread by con-

AN

INQUIRY

INTO

THE CAUSES AND EFFECTS

OF

THE VARIOLÆ VACCINÆ,

A DISEASE

DISCOVERED IN SOME OF THE WESTERN COUNTIES OF ENGLAND,

PARTICULARLY

GLOUCESTERSHIRE,

AND KNOWN BY THE NAME OF

THE COW POX.

———————

BY EDWARD JENNER, M.D. F.R.S. &c.

———————

——— QUID NOBIS CERTIUS IPSIS
SENSIBUS ESSE POTEST, QUO VERA AC FALSA NOTEMUS.

LUCRETIUS.

———————

London:

PRINTED, FOR THE AUTHOR,

BY SAMPSON LOW, Nº. 7, BERWICK STREET, SOHO:

AND SOLD BY LAW, AVE-MARIA LANE; AND MURRAY AND HIGHLEY, FLEET STREET

1798.

Title page from Jenner's book presenting his demonstration of the efficacy of vaccination in the control of smallpox.

*Edward Jenner, 1749–1823, to whom we owe vac-
cination against smallpox.*

tact. So after vaccination came into use, laws were
gradually passed prohibiting inoculation. But in the
years between, inoculation was resorted to by great
numbers of people; the New England papers of those
days contain many curious advertisements of inoculation farms where "gentlemen and ladies may retire
and take smallpox in a comfortable and safe manner."

Jenner was not the first to recognize the fact that
localized cowpox infection conferred immunity
against smallpox; that belief was a legend of the
dairy regions. But he took this country tradition
and demonstrated its validity as a scientific prin-

story, especaly the 32d, 57th and 18th, of the line; commanded by General Massena, and who in three days beat the enemy at St. Michel, at Rivoli and at Roverbella. The Roman legions marched 24 miles a-day. Ours marched 30, and fought also occasionally.

Citizens Dessaix, Chief of the 14th demi-brigade of light Infantry; Marquis, chief of the 29th; Fournesy, chief of the 17th; have been wounded Generals of Brigade, Vial, Brume, Bon, and Adjutant General Argod, particularly distinguished themselves.

The individual instances of bravery, are too numerous to be enumerated here

Signed, BUONAPARTE.

Capitulation made by the imperial troops under the walls of St. Georges, 27 Nivose, 5th year of the Republic.

Art. I. The honors of war granted, and all the troops prisoners of war.

II. The Officers shall retain their swords, their effects, and their equipage, and the soldiers their knap-sacks.

III. The General Officer, and other inferior officers may repair to their homes, if the General in chief consents to give them permission.—I engage my word and honour to inform the General in Chief that I engaged for this Article.

IV. Information shall be communicated to Marshal Count de Wurmser of the present Capitulation.

V. The sick and wounded shall be taken care of with all those sentiments of humanity

February 10.

We received this morning a letter from Dover, of which the following is an extract:

"I am sorry to acquaint you, that we are informed here that an embargo is laid on the other side from Brest to Dunkirk, which information was gained through a fishing-boat—I presume it must extend along the coast—how to credit this report I cannot as certain; but true it is, a secret expedition is going on at Dunkirk."

Admiral Duncan is expected in the North seas with a strong squadron. The greatest precautions are adopted in Yarmouth Roads to prevent a surprise. Ships are stationed at the entrances of the Roads, and watch boats are employed all night in rowing from one side of the channel to the other.

Letters have been received from Ireland which represent the internal state of the kingdom to be alarming.

INOCULATION.

THE subscriber respectfully informs the public that he has lately opened an Inoculation, at the pleasantly situated hospital in Glastenbury; Gentlemen and Ladies who wish to have the Small-Pox by this safe and easy method, may be boarded, and have faithful attendance paid them, by their obedient,

ASAPH COLEMAN.

March 25, 1797.

EIGHT months is allowed by the Court of Probate for the district of Hartford, for the creditors of the estate of Col Samuel Talcott, late of Hartford deceased;

An advertisement for inoculation against smallpox, Connecticut Courant, 1797.

ciple. The redoubtable John Hunter encouraged him and advised him in his work.

Jenner's experiments were simple, but they were crucial. What he did was to infect subjects with cowpox and then expose them to smallpox. They did not acquire the disease. In later years people who express doubt as to the real value of vaccination forget that practically all the early vaccinations, some thousands of them, were proved effective by subsequent attempts to produce smallpox by inoculation.

Philippe Pinel, 1745–1826, a pioneer in the humane care of the mentally ill.

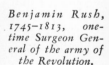

Benjamin Rush, 1745–1813, onetime Surgeon General of the army of the Revolution.

The antagonism to vaccination, still persisting feebly in some quarters, arose first from the resentment of the inoculators, who saw their vested interests impinged upon by a better method; later the opposition, or rather indifference, arose from forgetfulness or ignorance of what a horrible scourge smallpox was in the days before vaccination was introduced. Fielding Garrison has summed up the situation thus: "Propagandists . . . like Bernard Shaw, who regards it (vaccination) as a semi-savage rite, have been prone to forget the bevies of great ladies in the past whose pock-marked cuticles would cut but a sorry figure in these days of frank exposure." It is difficult for any of us living in these times, when preventive medicine has achieved great triumphs in freeing us from infections, to realize the enormous prevalence in the past of diseases such as smallpox, and plague, and typhus, and typhoid, and consumption. It has been only a little more than two centuries since, so it was said, "mothers counted their children only after they had had the smallpox."

Few if any men by their individual effort have contributed as greatly to social betterment as did the humanitarian Edward Jenner, the kindly country doctor of Gloucestershire.

Humanitarians of this kind, and there is no greater kind, bring us to the work of another physician of the 18th century whose endeavors were destined to influence profoundly our attitude toward the mentally ill. His work belongs really to the 19th century, for it was then that he published his book, *Traitè mèdico—philosophique sur l'alienation mentale,* and made his methods known. But it was on May 24, 1798, that the great and dramatic episode of the work of Philippe Pinel took place. That day, against the advice of authorities, he cut the chains from the mad men at Bicêtre. He treated these poor demented men and women as if they were ill, ill and deserving of sympathy and care. This was a new conception. In early times the insane had been venerated as prophets, as men set apart. Then during the first fifteen centuries of the Christian era they were treated as possessed of demons, exorcised and beaten. With the rise of interest in witchcraft many fell victims of that mania, and after it had died down the insane were treated as criminals, deliberately mischievous and stubborn, to be imprisoned, whipped, and brutalized. Pinel, in demonstrating that they were simply ill people, opened up the way for the modern care of the insane and for modern psychiatry.

We shall return to this subject of the medical humanitarians, for it is a strikingly new development and one particularly marked in the 19th century, of which we now approach the opening years. But first we pause to note a shift in the preëminent centers of medical education from Leyden and Paris to Vienna and Edinburgh. The old Vienna School, founded in this century, has its greatest importance in our narrative here because it was the site of the

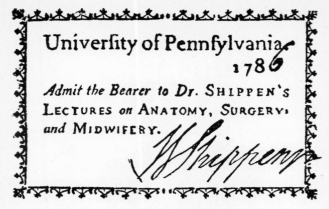

University of Pennfylvania
1786

Admit the Bearer to Dr. SHIPPEN'S
LECTURES *on* ANATOMY, SURGERY,
and MIDWIFERY.

*Ticket of admission to William Shippen, Jr.'s. lectures on
anatomy at Philadelphia*

work of Ignatz Semmelweis, who, in the 19th century, is to make the first practical step toward the
control of puerperal infection. The rise of Edinburgh
to medical eminence, largely as the result of the
family of Monroes, has a local interest in the fact
that the most prominent physicians of Colonial
America, John Morgan, William Shippen, Jr., and
Benjamin Rush, received their training there. Each
of these men in turn served as Surgeon General in
the war of the Revolution. They were pioneers in
medical development and medical education in our
country, but in the last analysis they left no contributions to medical progress that bring them into
peerage with the characters who in this brief outline we have paused to touch upon.

*Ignatz Philipp Semmelweis, 1818–1865, a pioneer
in obstetrical asepsis.*

But in touching only upon such men we leave perhaps a false impression of the level to which medical
practice had attained. There is nearly always a great
lag between discovery and application; it was vastly
greater in those days than it is today. The work of
Paracelsus, Vesalius, and Paré had made their mark
on medical education. The average physician of the
18th century was perhaps better acquainted with
anatomy than was the physician of the 17th century.
But all in all the average medical practice, particularly surgical practice, was at a low level. The better
physicians, better usually because of some marked

felicity of personality, occupied high social positions and were influential men, as in the case of Benjamin Rush. Most of them were addicted to affectations which would be looked upon today as smacking strongly of charlatanism: dashing, gaudy carriages, powdered wigs, satin breeches, gold-headed canes, and muffs to protect the hands and preserve the "tactus eruditus" were the order of the day, as were also a pompous mien and an air of infallibility. It was a time when art and personality and show rather than science ruled medical practice.

Many of the most successful "physicians" of the time had no medical education whatever. The 18th century was preëminently the era of famous quacks. Such names have come down to us as those of Mesmer, and William Read, a tailor who acted as ophthalmologist to Queen Anne and Gibbon the historian, and Joshua, or "Spot", Ward, who gave medical aid to George II, and Sally Mapp, the bone-setter who with her ilk was caricatured in Hogarth's famous engraving of charlatans, "The Undertakers' Arms."

In the same 18th century both Queen Anne and Louis XVI carried out the old superstition of touching for the King's Evil.

Physics, Chemistry, and Mathematics Enter Medicine

WE PASS now into the 19th century, but as far as medical progress is concerned, the transition is imperceptible. There are no indications, unless it be the amazing demonstration of the efficacy of vaccination by Jenner, that medicine is destined to undergo a revolution as profound as the social revolution thru which mankind of the period is passing. The American Rebellion is scarcely passed; the French Revolution is still seething; the industrial revolution is gaining impetus. The common man is attaining a new importance; labor with hands, with brain, is acquiring a new dignity. And medicine? In answer compare a physician of the opening years of the 19th century with one at the opening of the 20th century; compare what they are capable of offering to the patient and to the public. As men, in character, they have changed little perhaps; their aims, their interests, their devotion to their ideals have not altered, for these things are inherent parts of the humanitarian calling they have chosen, handed down from the priests of Aesculapius, the heritage of every reputable physician in every age. Wherein they have changed is this: knowledge, first. A century which gave the physician such fundamental principles as the cellular pathology of Virchow and the bacterial cause of infection, which gave such revolutionary discoveries as that of anesthesia and antisepsis, could not fail to alter the entire scope of medical practice. Knowledge, first; then a change, a profound change, in education. It was in this century that the discoveries of chemistry and physics were widely applied to physiological problems. The principles which Harvey had used and the experimental approach which at the hands of Jenner had yielded vaccinations became a part, an accepted part, of medical education and delineated the mode of thought of the trained physician. Knowledge, then a change in education, and then further a change in the social situation of medicine. The medical advances of the 19th century, particularly those arising from the demonstration of the bacterial cause of infection, made medicine a social necessity and in fact a guiding force in modern civilization. Practical preventive medicine, destined to reach its greatest impetus in the 20th century, was launched in the 19th century. As a result, the physician, who up to this time had confined himself in medical matters almost solely to the bedside of his patient, now moved out into a broader field; all society, not only the individual man, but mankind as a whole, became his patient. The city, the state, the country—in fact, the world—was to be guarded against disease. The physician had fought the good battle at the bedside; now he was to fight it in the front ranks of an advancing civilization.

The physician at the close of the 19th century was a different man from the one whom we met at the opening of the 19th century, as different as were his surroundings, due to the inventive improvements of this century; the stage coach, the sailboat, the candle, the filthy city without sewers during this period gave way in turn to the railroad and the automobile, the steamboat, the paraffin lamp and then the electric light, and the modern clean city with sewers, with pure water, and with clean streets and clean homes. And this last and important change, the one that made the modern city possible, was entirely an outgrowth of medical advancement.

The physician had changed. His surroundings had changed. And as this alteration developed and life became easier, and, above all, safer, for man, the humanitarian outlook of the public changed. We have mentioned the work of Philippe Pinel, who was among the first to change our regard toward the insane, who gave us, indeed, the first impetus toward discarding this word with its connotation of the court and the prison and toward adopting the term which signifies the humanitarian advancement, the term mentally ill. And with him stands another practical humanitarian, the American, Dorothea Lynde Dix of Boston, who literally forced upon a reluctant public the duty of providing for the mentally ill. She in the 'forties and 'fifties of the 19th century was responsible for the founding of more than thirty of our state institutions for this purpose.

We can appreciate the movement of public sentiment toward practical humanitarianism only by retrospect. At the opening of the 19th century injustice, cruelty, outrage, were accepted as the normal and the natural. There was no Red Cross

agreement between belligerents in war time; there
had been isolated examples of such but they were
rarities. At the close of the 19th century the International Red Cross and its humanitarian purposes
were subscribed to fully by the public, a public whose
ancestors of less than a hundred years before had in
war time seen the physician shot as a belligerent and
who had made no organized effort to provide for the
wounded upon the battle-field.

Perhaps no humanitarian change ever effected has
been of more practical importance to the ill than
that which in the middle of this same century Florence Nightingale brought into being in the dark
wards of the barrack hospital of Scutari. Florence
Nightingale did not found nursing, for nursing is
as old as the human race; what she did was to or-
ganize nursing, make it a dignified profession for
trained gentlewomen and one with a high *esprit de
corps* among its members. She organized nursing—
that word organized is the very keynote of the medical progress of the 19th century. We shall return
to it in a moment. But before we leave the changing
public of the 19th century, let us record the fact
that the progress towards practical humanitarianism,
witnessed equally in no other century, was largely
under the leadership of medicine. When some day
the humanitarian, rather than the warrior or trader,
takes his rightful stand in the pages of history, then
and for the first time we shall find these pages replete with the names of physicians. And what a

*Florence Nightingale, "the Lady with the Lamp," 1823–1910,
who by her example during the Crimean War made nursing a
respectable occupation for gentlewomen.*

I am myself always a
prisoner from illness &
overwork. but all the
more wishes for godspeed

Florence Nightingale

Note in the handwriting of Florence Nightingale.

contribution the 19th century will make with names such as Morton and Long, and Wells, and Pasteur, and Koch, and Lister, and Reed; for they are men who have altered our ways of living, our ways of thinking, more profoundly than the warriors, and the traders, and even the philosophers of all ages.

During our digression here we mentioned organization as the keynote of medical progress in the 19th century. We applied it in connection with Florence Nightingale's work in training nurses; we could have mentioned it equally with the Red Cross movement, with the endeavors of Dorothea Dix, in regard to medical education, and in medical research. But let us turn to one less obvious but none-the-less important aspect of this movement toward organization and correlation, to one which in great measure made the medical advancement of the 19th century possible.

The application of the sciences of chemistry, physics, and mathematics in the field of invention produced the industrial revolution, and they made available to us the products of engineering which have been so highly developed in our present century. These same basic sciences applied to the problems of medicine have yielded much of the modern advancement in this field. But the relation does not end there. The development of industry and the development of modern medical practice have in turn been directly related. It has been through the aid of industry that many of the life-saving measures of modern therapy have become practical realities. And it is this practicality of modern medicine that differentiates it so strikingly from the medicine of previous centuries.

In bygone days the medicaments used by physicians were of simple nature, simple, that is, in the source of the ingredients. They could be readily prepared by the individual pharmacist. They were derived mainly from readily accessible natural sources. As late as the beginning of the 19th century the complicated chemical compounds and even more complicated biological preparations indispensable to the medical practice of the 20th century were undreamed of. The dispensing pharmacist, unaided, could supply the physicians' needs; indeed in those days many physicians prepared their own medicaments. To characterize the state of affairs one need only to recall the vaccine virus of the early 19th century; in those days a scab was plucked from the arm of the vaccinated patient and carried in the pocket of the physician until needed; he then pared off a portion, no doubt with his pocket knife, and in a scratch on the arm of his patient made with the point of this same useful knife, placed the paring. It was simple, straightforward procedure, characteristic of the period, but one which in a day that has seen the demonstration of the bacterial cause of infection brings not a feeling of admiration for the rugged simplicity of early 19th century medicine but instead one of horror.

The vaccine of today is of a purity attained in few products outside the biological, pharmaceutical and chemical products now in use.

But purity, with all of the elaborate safeguards, the repeated tests, the standardization—things upon which manufacturing reputations are built—represents only one phase of the coöperation between industry and medicine. The other is a bond direct with medical research. A research worker in one of the great universities or hospitals finds a chemical compound, a vaccine, or an anti-toxin which is beneficial in preventing or curing disease, but such discovery remains only of academic interest unless the product can be made readily available to the practicing physicians. Neither the physician nor the dispensing pharmacist is equipped to prepare the product himself; nor is the research worker in a position to manufacture and distribute it. At this point the manufacturing chemist, distributing through the dispensing pharmacist, steps in and supplies the indispensable link between the medical research worker on the one hand and the practicing physician on the other. Industry has thus contributed to make medical advancement possible and practical.

We have devoted many pages here to things far in advance of our running story of medical progress. But these social and industrial correlations are as much the flesh and sinew of modern medical progress as is medical discovery itself.

Great Personalities Outrun Research

LET us turn back to the beginning of the period which was to witness the great revolution in medicine; let us stand once more upon the threshold of the 19th century. It is a barren period for medical discovery. There are great personalities of medical and surgical practice, men like Broussais and Dupuytren, but they dominate by strength of personality alone rather than by virtue of any lasting fundamental contribution to medical progress. And as one approaches nearer and nearer to the present times, it becomes increasingly difficult in a brief survey to evaluate contributions purely aside from personality. Medicine more than any other field that touches upon science puts a premium upon the personality of its members, for medicine is still, and for long years to come will remain, in measure an art. Some of the cherished medical characters of the 19th and 20th centuries achieved eminence mainly thru strength of personality. They were great characters, but in the passage of years, when their disciples are gone, they will be forgotten. On the other hand, time, unless our whole civilization crumbles with it, will not obliterate the names of the men and women to whom we owe the fundamental knowledge which has made medical progress. It must be deeds, not men, that are to illuminate our story.

The first forty years of the 19th century witnessed little of the momentous movement toward modern

medicine; much of the sterile theorization characteristic of the 18th century carried over into this
period. But there are some careful observers of disease who have left us classical descriptions, and there
are many new and useful chemicals discovered or
isolated. In the midst of these scattered contributions
there are three outstanding events: the discovery of
the stethoscope, the founding of medical statistics,
and the demonstration of the cellular structure of
plant and animal tissue.

We mention here, for classical descriptions of diseases, the account of arteriosclerosis by Antonio
Scarpa, James Parkinson's on paralysis agitans, Pierre
Bretonneau on diphtheria, William Gerhard on typhus and typhoid, Robert Adams on heart block,
Richard Bright on essential nephritis and yellow
atrophy of the liver, Sir Dominic Corrigan on aortic
insufficiency, and Abraham Colles on the transmission of congenital syphilis.

In these same forty years occurred in America the
historically famous operation of Ephriam McDowell
—the successful removal of an ovarian cyst, an operation duplicated by the great American founder of
medical schools, Nathan Smith. Of greater importance were the experiments of William Beaumont,
who studied gastric digestion on Alexis St. Martin,
a half-breed trader in whose abdominal wall as the
result of a gunshot wound there was a persistent
opening into the stomach. His work takes its place
with the only other important experimental physiol-

Ephriam McDowell, 1771–1830, a practitioner in the then frontier town of Danville, Ky., the first surgeon to perform an ovariotomy.

Richard Bright, 1789–1858; he described essential nephritis, Bright's disease.

ogy of this period—the demonstration of the function of the nerve root by Sir Charles Bell of London.

For the events with the greatest influence upon medical progress we have selected first in order of chronology the discovery of the stethoscope by René Laennec. This young Frenchman, who was himself suffering from tuberculosis, did more than discover the first precise method of diagnosis for this disease; he described the pathology of tuberculosis.

The next event of major importance was the founding of medical statistics by Pierre Louis, also of France. In 1835 he demonstrated by statistical proof that the extensive blood-letting then in vogue was of little value in treating pneumonia. The importance of his work lies not in the subject he attacked but in the method he employed.

The final event we have chosen occurred in the last years of these four decades; in 1839 Theodor Schwann of Germany enunciated the fact that the cell is the structural unit of all living things.

Perhaps before leaving this period we can add one social change affecting medicine: it was in these years that the "anatomy laws" providing subjects for dissection were formulated. This move did much to alleviate the intense popular opposition then existing against this branch of medical study, an opposition which in this country culminated in the "Doctors Mob" of New York City in the closing years of the 18th century; it was necessary to call out the militia to quell this rising against the hospital and the physi-

*René Théophile Hyacinthe Laennec, 1781–1826, the
originator of the stethoscope.*

cians. The beneficial "anatomy laws" were formulated soon after the disreputable Burke and Hare
affair of Scotland, the "anatomy murders" of 1827–
29, in which these two worthies undertook to pro-
cure subjects for the anatomy rooms of the medical
schools by the murder of inconspicuous citizens.

Grouped together here as are the advances of this
period, they seem numerous perhaps, but this period
covers nearly half a century; it is only following it
that the progress gains its acceleration. We can no
longer deal with centuries as a whole or even half

centuries, for decade by decade come the great discoveries which have shaped modern medicine.

America Begins to Contribute

IN THE decade 1840 to 1850 we find a continuation
of the description of diseases with the fidelity that
Hippocrates had employed. It is in this period that
Carl Basedow described exophthalmic goiter, that
William Stokes recorded his classical account of heart
block, that Thomas Addison wrote on pernicious
anemia, and that Rudolf Virchow commenced his
studies that were to be consummated in his great
thesis of cellular pathology.

It is in this period that Claude Bernard founded
experimental medicine. In 1843 he commenced his
study of the glycogenic function of the liver. Barely
ten years before he had come to Paris an aspirant to
be a dramatic poet. Two men influenced his career
and led him on his way towards his great physiological contributions. To Saint-Marc Girardin, the critic,
who advised him to give up poetry and try medicine,
and to his teacher, the great Magendie, medicine
owes an everlasting debt.

At the same time that Bernard was founding experimental medicine in France, the Weber brothers,
Ernst and Eduard, were carrying out their investigations in Leipzig, and showing that impulses in the
vagus nerve affect the action of the heart—one of
the fundamental discoveries of physiology.

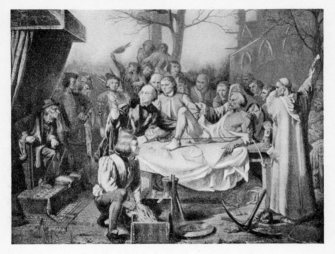

An operation for the bladder stone carried out before Louis XI of France.

And now it is in this decade that for the first time we turn to America for a great medical discovery. Next to Jenner's vaccination it is the most useful and certainly the most humane that has been made in all the centuries that we have passed thru in this outline. It is the discovery of a practical anesthesia for surgical operations.

Attempts to deaden the pain of surgical operation were made at earlier dates; Dioscorides, the surgeon of Nero, described a soporific mixture for this purpose, and the surgeons at the School of Salerno employed what was called a soporific sponge. Opium and alcohol found their use for this same purpose.

But none was satisfactory; none brought appreciable relief to the frightful suffering of the patient undergoing operation in all the centuries before the 4th decade of the 19th. In fact by the 16th century they were largely discontinued; thus in the works of such surgeons as Paré we find no mention of their use. Without anesthesia operations were performed only for direst necessity; the shrieking patient was held on the table by strong men; the surgeon, to the detriment of his skill but in the interests of mercy, was as speedy in his manipulations as was possible. Indeed some of the more deft surgeons were little short of sleight-of-hand artists; they could amputate a limb so rapidly that close attention was necessary on the part of spectators or they missed seeing the operation entirely.

Shortly before ether anesthesia was demonstrated there was much discussion of the use of the hypnotic trance during operations. Altho it was said to have been employed at times in the Orient, it did not prove practical in the West. Nothing shows the complete absence of any means of alleviating the pain of operation more clearly than the fact that the very words anesthesia and anesthetic were not in use prior to 1846. After the demonstration of ether anesthesia in the Massachusetts General Hospital that year these words were suggested by Oliver Wendell Holmes.

It is a commonplace that the same invention or discovery is often made almost simultaneously in widely separated places. The time seems ripe for it,

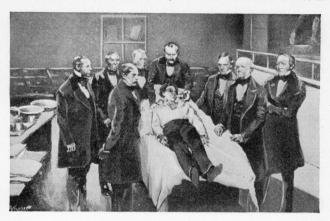

The first public demonstration of surgical anesthesia, Massachusetts General Hospital, October 16, 1846.

virtually demands it, and, as if by magic, it appears. Thus it was with anesthesia. It was discovered, we might say, three times in three different places within a period of four years. In the interests of medical priority the important fact is that all three of these places were in the United States—Georgia, Connecticut, and Massachusetts. In chronology the events occurred thus. Crawford Long of Georgia in 1842 used ether during a minor surgical operation. This fact remained unknown except locally for several years. But in the meantime, in 1843, Horace Wells, a dentist of Hartford, Connecticut, observed the apparent deadening of sensation induced by nitrous oxide as administered during a popular demonstration of scientific matters given by an itinerant lecturer named Colton. Wells tried nitrous oxide with success in the extraction of a tooth. He did more; he attempted to interest the surgeons of the Massachusetts General Hospital in the possibility of using nitrous oxide during surgical operations. But the demonstration that he gave at that institution— the extraction of a tooth—was not successful. However, following his example, William Morton, a dentist of Charlton, Massachusetts, and a student at the Harvard Medical School, attempted to find a more satisfactory anesthetic agent. It is possible that his attention was directed to ether by the advice of Charles Jackson. In any event Morton tried ether experimentally, and finally, on October 16, 1846, with the permission of John Warren, Chief Surgeon of the Massachusetts General Hospital, he administered it to a patient of that institution during a surgical operation. The demonstration was a complete success, and the facts of it were widely published.

There are two more events concerning anesthesia to be recorded in this period. One is the discovery of the anesthetic properties of chloroform by James Simpson of Scotland. Following the reports of Morton's demonstration, he tried ether but, dissatisfied, searched for a substitute and came upon chloroform. He was an obstetrician. His use of anesthesia to alleviate the pains of childbirth was violently opposed by the Scottish clergy on the grounds that pain was ordained by the scriptural command, "In sorrow thou

Edward Robinson Squibb (1819–1900)
American Scientist, Physician, and Chemist

He was a pioneer in the standardization and purification of medicinal products. His name became synonymous with high ideals in medicine and pharmacy.

shalt bring forth children", and that it was impious to attempt to avert it by anesthetic agents. And it was Simpson who stilled this opposition by his own famous quotation from scripture; he pointed out that when Eve was born, God cast Adam into a deep sleep before performing upon him the notable costalectomy. Anesthesia was thus permissible by scriptural precedent.

The final events connected with the introduction of ether anesthesia occurred in America. In 1852

Dr. E. R. Squibb first manufactured pure anesthetic ether by steam in place of the open-fire method in common use.

During the year 1853 Squibb perfected his continuous process for the manufacture of ether in a still specially devised by him, thus making an important, and, indeed, the last, great contribution to ether anesthesia.

Throughout the trying period of the Civil War and thereafter, the work of Dr. Squibb was devoted to the purification and the setting up of quality standards and the devising of processes and apparatus for the manufacture of medicinal products.

The momentous discovery of anesthesia would seem almost sufficient for the contributions of one country in one decade. But 1840 to 1850 is pre-eminently the American decade. It was then that the surgeon Marion Sims of South Carolina and later of New York developed his famous operation for the then irreparable condition of vesicovaginal fistula. His work, which became widely known in the next decade, greatly influenced gynecological surgery. It was Sims who established the New York State Hospital for Women, which in the 'fifties and 'sixties of the 19th century was the center of the best gynecological work in the world. In 1894 a statue was erected to Marion Sims in Bryant Park, New York City, one of the few emblems of the kind commemorating the physicians of this country.

It was in this same decade of the 'forties in

Oliver Wendell Holmes, from a drawing made by himself, 1809–1894; he was the first to point out the contagious nature of puerperal fever.

America that Dorothea Dix, whom we have mentioned as one of the greatest humanitarians, carried out her pioneer work on the care of the mentally ill.

And finally in the same decade and in the same country Oliver Wendell Holmes read before the Boston Society for Medical Improvement his paper *On the Contagiousness of Puerperal Fever*. In this essay he points out as probable the very things that within five years are to be proved independently by Ignatz Semmelweis of Vienna: that puerperal fever,

then an ever-present danger to the parturient woman, was carried from patient to patient by the
unclean hands of the physician. Holmes said it could
be prevented; Semmelweis showed that it could be.

Holmes's words were met with hostility; Semmelweis's demonstration was laughed down, derided.
Yet the work of these men, as we know now, ranks
as great or perhaps greater than the demonstration
of ether anesthesia. There are few lives more tragic
and few more useful than that of the Hungarian
physician Semmelweis, assistant in the obstetrical
wards of the Allgemeines Krankenhaus in Vienna.
The ward of the hospital was divided into two sections, one for the training of midwives and the other
for the training of physicians. In the ward devoted
to the midwives the mortality from puerperal fever
was low; in that used to train physicians the mortality from this disease was high. The reason for this
difference was Semmelweis's problem. The first clue
to the solution came when his friend Kolletschka
died following a dissection wound; his symptoms
were similar to those of the women who succumbed
to puerperal fever. Semmelweis reasoned that Kolletschka had died because putrid material was introduced into his body; he reasoned that the women
died for the same reason, and that the source of the
contagion was the unclean hands of the students
who examined them. He then forced everyone at-
tending the ward to wash their hands in chloride of
lime. In consequence the mortality among the women

Horace Wells, 1815–1848; his use of nitrous oxide for dental extraction was the inspiration of William Morton's use of ether for surgical operation.

William Thomas Green Morton, 1819–1868; he made the famous demonstration of surgical anesthesia at the Massachusetts General Hospital, October 16, 1846.

dropped to a level almost unbelievably low for lying-in wards of that time, it fell from 9.92 per cent to 1.27 per cent.

Semmelweis had anticipated Koch and Pasteur with the conception of blood poisoning from infection; he had anticipated Lister with the idea of antiseptics. But he came too early; another decade or two or three were needed yet before the time was ripe for his discovery. He was laughed at, persecuted. In disgust he left Vienna and went to Budapest, a broken man, to die within a few years, insane.

A Decade of Methods

IT WAS in the decade following the one which had seen the work of Long and Wells, and Morton, and Sims, and Holmes, and Semmelweis that Florence Nightingale reorganized nursing. In this the Victorian period the level of nursing had sunk very low indeed. The hospitals were dirty; the patients poorly cared for. Actual nursing was relegated to a degraded type of woman of low intelligence, often dissolute, still more often dishonest—the type that Dickens has portrayed as Sairey Gamp. Even the Sisters of Charity were so hampered by regulations that in many cases they could do little more than shed an air of genteel serenity over the wards in their charge. The actual care of the sick was considered a degrading occupation. Their consequent neglect is writ large in the mortality of the day. Florence

Carl Siegmund Credé, 1819–1892; he is notable for his method of manual expression of the placenta and for his prophylactic measure against ophthalmia of the newborn.

Nightingale, anxious to find a useful occupation for intelligent women in a time when woman's place was considered to be strictly in the home, turned to nursing. Her example was not followed, however, until after the Crimean War, for during that war, at the filthy barrack hospitals, she gave a practical demonstration of the importance of good nursing in helping the patient to live. Her example created a wave of enthusiasm for this new occupation of gentlewomen, and soon funds were raised and the training of nurses instituted.

In this same decade, 1850 to 1860, we find, as in previous decades, classical descriptions of disease states; Brown-Séquard described unilateral paralysis, Octave Landry described ascending paralysis, Thomas Addison published his account of the disturbance of the adrenal gland, and Albrecht von Graefe gave the clear details of retinal embolism.

New drugs, but possibly in fewer number, became available this decade; cocaine and physostigmin were the more important ones. But in spite of the isolation of cocaine, local anesthesia was not to come into use for nearly three decades more. Perhaps the outstanding chemical contribution to medicine, but, like local anesthesia, one to be applied much later, was the synthesis of aniline dyes by Perkins, which paved the way for the preparation of many indispensable medicaments. And in connection with the new therapeutic measures of this decade there follows naturally mention of the fact that it was then that the hypodermic syringe found its first uses in America.

It was then also that Carl Credé of Leipzig made his important contribution to obstetrics—the manual expression of the placenta. Three decades later he was to introduce his prophylaxis against ophthalmia of the newborn, the installation of silver nitrate solution at birth. Equally important to infant life was the development of the method of intubation of the larynx in diphtheria. It was first used in this decade by Eugène Bouchut at Paris, but it was thru the later work of Joseph O'Dwyer of Cleveland,

Ohio, that the method was developed into full, practical usefulness. Intubation was needed much in these years, for diphtheria was on the increase; the mode of its spread was not yet known, nor had antitoxin been discovered.

This seems to be a decade of important methods —the tube for the larynx and then the laryngoscope, invented by a Spanish singing teacher in London, Manuel Garcia, and then the ophthalmoscope, originated by Hermann von Helmholtz, then at Königsberg. He followed it with his ophthalmometer, with which he was able to elucidate the mechanism of accommodation. Important as are these practical contributions of the great Helmholtz, his most fundamental work was in the field of mathematical physics, to which more and more modern medicine is turning for the explanation of the phenomena of health and disease.

There are great names in the basic sciences this decade: Helmholtz; Claude Bernard, who at this time has discovered the vaso constrictor mechanism of the arterioles; Augustus Waller, who has described the process of degeneration of nerves; and Carl Ludwig, from whom dates, as every medical student has learned, many of the mechanical methods of recording physiological phenomena.

It was in the years 1850 to 1860 that Charles Darwin published his *Origin of Species;* equally fundamental was Rudolf Virchow's *Cellular Pathology.* Virchow was born in Pomerania, worked for the

Prussian Government, and was professor of pathology at Berlin. He was the strong character of the medicine of the 19th century; more than any other man he broke down the lingering tendencies to theorize, the besetting and persisting sin of 18th century medicine. Not only did he influence medicine toward scientific accuracy of procedure, but, greatest of all, he founded modern pathology. He carried pathology to its ultimate, to the cell and the cell contents.

Virchow brings us well into modern times—he lived until 1902 and was known to many men still living. But the decade in which he published his monumental work was still in advance of the greatest practical discovery of modern medicine—the bacterial cause of infection. For it is not until the period from 1860 to 1870 that we find the first indications of the enormous benefits that are eventually to be derived from the discovery. It was in this decade that Lister established the antiseptic principle in surgery. And linked with Lister's name must be that of Pasteur, for altho that great chemist had not yet done his work on human disease, he had nevertheless shown that bacteria are the cause of putrefaction.

The Cause of Infection Discovered

IT IS difficult to realize that in a decade which gave such fundamental work as that of Virchow, in one

Joseph Lister, 1827–1912, the founder of the antiseptic principle.

which was so near to our own time, the cause of infection was not known, that men still believed that a miasma, an emanation from marshes, poisoned wounds and caused fevers. Take away from modern medical practice, from modern life, the knowledge that we have concerning bacterial infection, and our medical practice and in fact our urban mode of living would regress a full seventy years. Public health as we know it and sanitation would be essentially non-existent.

When Lister, the English Quaker surgeon, became in 1860 professor of surgery in the University of Glasgow, wound infection was expected in practically every surgical case; and the expectation was fulfilled with the most frightful types of septicemia and putrid gangrene. But there was one exception, and it was this exception that caught Lister's attention. Simple fractures did not lead to pus formation; all other wounds did. Now the only difference, so Lister reasoned, between the open wound and the wound in the simple fracture, was that one was exposed to the air and the other was not. Something in the air, then, must cause the infection, that is, the pus and the putrefaction in the open wound. Dissatisfied with the belief of miasmas, he turned to Pasteur's work. He showed that bacteria cause putrefaction in wounds. Lister attempted to kill the bacteria and to keep them out of the wounds. He thus founded the principle of antisepsis. And when subsequent work showed that much of the infection came not from the air but from the dirty hands of surgeons and wound dressers, this antiseptic principle grew into the aseptic principle.

Modern surgery, surgery of the abdomen, the brain, the chest, the joints, dates from Lister's time. But it did not at once assume the form in which we know it today. In the years between there were great pioneers of modern surgical technique, men such as Theodor Billroth, Ernst von Bergmann, and William Halsted.

So overwhelming is this discovery of a means of controlling infection that it overshadows all other advances of the period. Yet it was in this decade that

William Stewart Halsted, 1852–1922, one of the founders of modern surgical technique.

Julius Cohnheim, Virchow's pupil and, like him, a native of Pomerania, established the modern conception of the inflammatory process and the formation of pus. It was in the same period that Max von Pettenkofer of Bavaria, who later headed the first institute of hygiene, obtained with Carl von Voit the basic knowledge of energy metabolism. It was in this decade that Carl Wunderlich, teaching at Leipzig, wrote his classical treatise on bodily temperature and disease. The practical use of the clinical thermometer dates from his time. He broke down the old conception that fever was a disease entity and showed that it was merely a symptom.

Two more outstanding events of medical importance occurred at this time, but both found their usefulness in later years. Gregor Mendel, an Augustinian monk of Brünn, reported his results from experiments in hybridizing peas. This document of his lay unnoticed for nearly thirty-five years. And then finally at the beginning of the 20th century it came into prominence as the basic, or Mendelian, law of inheritance.

The other event arose from the work of Charles Brown-Séquard of this country and of France, who carried on the work of Claude Bernard in experimental medicine. His greatest importance here lies in his direct postulation of the doctrine of internal secretions, a conception that in later years was to show the way to the many useful therapeutic measures of organotherapy, and to provide as well an understanding of the chemical control of bodily functions.

And finally, in closing this decade, we find another of the great humanitarian movements for which the 19th century is so notable. This one was carried out in the true spirit of a century in which the keynote was organization. In 1864 at Geneva was held a conference which resulted in the founding of the International Red Cross. The man who conceived the idea of a people united to help the sufferers in war and in disaster was a Swiss, Henri

Louis Pasteur, 1822–1895.

Dunant. In his honor the Swiss Flag was adapted to form the symbol of the new organization.

Preventive Medicine Begins

Turning now to the years 1870 to 1880, we come very near to our own times, as we finally reach the decade in which the bacterial cause of infection was established—probably the most far-reaching discovery in all human progress. Like Lister's discovery of the previous decade, the work of Pasteur and Koch overshadows all other medical events of the time. Yet this was the period when Weir Mitchell introduced the rest cure, Max Nitze the cystoscope, and when Paget made his classical description of osteitis deformans. But despite these contributions Pasteur and Koch dominate the field.

Louis Pasteur was born at Dôle. He studied chemistry at Paris. He was not a physician; he came into the medical field only as his discoveries led him there. And his work in this direction started with the purely lay problem of why wine spoils, a problem of great economic importance to the French. Pasteur studied fermentation and he studied putrefaction. He was able to show that putrefaction resulted from the contamination and subsequent growth of bacteria. To prevent this bacterial growth he developed the process of heating the fluid, known now by his name as pasteurization. It was this work that caught Lister's attention and led him on to the discovery of the cause of wound infection.

But Pasteur went further than Lister, for he conceived the idea that bacteria were the cause of the various febrile diseases transmitted from person to person. It is in the next decade and the next that we shall deal with his efforts to control disease, which resulted in the development of vaccines and in the prophylactic virus against rabies.

In the meantime we turn to Robert Koch, a country doctor of Prussia, who as a hobby peered at all manner of things under his microscope. Bacteria attracted his attention. He studied anthrax and

Robert Koch, 1843–1910, the founder of modern bacteriology.

worked out in his crude laboratory the complete life-history of this organism. He demonstrated conclusively that the anthrax bacillus is the cause of a disease from which sheep and cattle and sometimes men suffered. Pasteur postulated the theory of infection; Koch proved it. He did more; he laid the very foundations of modern bacteriological technique.

It was in 1882 that Koch, now a member of the Imperial Health Department, made the momentous discovery of the cause of tuberculosis; that year he isolated the tubercle bacillus and showed that the

disease could develop only after infection with this
organism. He thus opened the way for the eradication of a disease which at that time was the "Captain of the Men of Death."

Koch's discovery of the tubercle bacillus takes us
into the decade 1880 to 1890. As would naturally
be expected, the discoveries of Koch and Pasteur
were attracting world-wide attention at that time,
and there was an active search for all disease bacteria, with the result that the majority of the more
important pathogenic organisms were identified: the
bacilli of cholera, typhoid, diphtheria, tetanus, and
meningitis, to name only a few. And it was equally
natural that men should seek to protect themselves
against bacteria; hence it was in this decade that we
have the investigations of bacteria in milk, the first
step towards the pure milk of today, a movement
that has had an enormous influence upon the decline
in infant mortality. Sanitation, sewage disposal, and
the purification of water, measures that make modern urban civilization possible, had purpose given
to them as the result of the bacterial discoveries of
this and the previous decade.

Save for Jenner's discovery of nearly a hundred
years before, preventive medicine had its origin in
this decade, not only the broad aspects of general
prevention, but specific prevention as well. It was
then that Pasteur discovered the principles of vaccines and proved their value in anthrax and chicken
cholera. The work was carried on to the disease

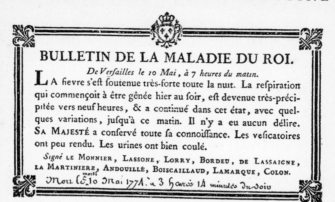

Bulletin issued by the physicians of Louis XV during his fatal attack of smallpox. He was the last important personage to die of this disease.

typhoid fever by André Chantemesse and Fernand Widal, the latter of whom in the next decade was to discover the principle of bacterial agglutination and devise the test which bears his name. The possibilities of altering the virulence of organisms, in addition to immediate practical results in the work on vaccines, threw light into the whole subject of the natural history of diseases, the rise and fall of virulence, and the genesis of epidemics.

It was then also that Pasteur announced his discovery of a method of preventing rabies—the Pasteur prophylactic treatment. It is difficult for us now even to imagine what a dreadful threat rabies had been, especially to the mother of a child, in those days when there was no way of preventing this invariably fatal disease.

From the prophylactic treatment of rabies, from vaccines, we go one step further in the great medical discoveries of the closing decade of the 19th century. We turn again to Koch's Institute at Berlin, where the Prussian army surgeon Emil von Behring is studying the toxins of bacteria. Already Pasteur has noticed that the bacterium of chicken cholera discharges a poison into the fluid in which it is grown, and his pupils, Roux and Yersin, have obtained the same results with the diphtheria bacillus—they have found diphtheria toxin. It is Emil von Behring who, studying this toxin, discovers the principle of antitoxin formation within the body. He is able to prepare a therapeutic serum—diphtheria antitoxin. And soon a second antitoxin—one against tetanus— is to be perfected.

Vaccines, the prophylactic treatment against rabies, antitoxin—any of these discoveries which we touch upon so briefly here would have illuminated a whole century, as Jenner's work did one hundred years before. But here in the closing years of the 19th century discoveries that have altered the condition of men's lives more profoundly than have any social or economic advances, came one upon the other. Contrast this period with the sterile years of the Middle Ages, the faltering, halting progress of the Renaissance and the two centuries after it, and we obtain some conception of what the 19th century

*Major Walter Reed, 1851–1902, who headed the
"yellow fever commission" which demonstrated the
rôle of the mosquito in the transmission of yellow
fever.*

medical revolution meant to mankind in relieving
the age-long and constant threat of disease.

And, as we have said before, it was a revolution
made practical by organization, by coöperation.
The rapidly advancing sciences of chemistry and
physics formed the sources upon which medicine
drew for its researches; the coöperation of industry
rendered these researches of practical benefit in making the health-saving, life-saving products of research available to every physician.

It is hardly necessary to give here a list of diseases in which treatment or prevention has been singularly advanced by such coöperation. We have seen how rabies has been eradicated because of the general availability of a prophylactic treatment. The amazing discovery that an antitoxin could be prepared which would neutralize the toxin of diphtheria provided a specific and powerful treatment for this disease and has resulted in a very material decrease in child mortality. Recently in the progress and control of scarlet fever results comparable with those which have meant so much for the reduction of diphtheria are being accomplished.

The preventive measures of this decade do not stop with vaccines and antitoxins, for it was between the years 1880-1890 that prophylaxis against specific organism had its origin. It was then that Carl Credé advanced his method of preventing ophthalmia in the newborn. It was to be some twenty years more before a similar prophylactic procedure was to be developed by Elie Metchnikoff for the disease syphilis. But the measure for the control of this once great scourge of mankind, the one which had filled the surgical wards with patients to be operated upon for aneurism, which had wrought a social havoc with its tabetic, paretic, and congenital forms, are events of later decades—the greatest glory of 20th century medicine. Before they could be developed, men were to learn that bacteria are not the only cause of infectious diseases. And it was in this decade which we are dealing with now, 1880-1890, that the preliminary steps move in that direction. The biologists had already established the fact that such animals as the frog have protozoan parasites; the life history and even the occurrence of intermediary hosts had been worked out. But there was no conception that human diseases might arise from similar animal parasites until Alphonse Laveran of Paris discovered the parasite of malaria.

Laveran's discovery, important as it was, did not supply means of controlling malaria. The knowledge of the transmission of the parasite by the mosquito was needed before his discovery could grow to practical usefulness. For in this decade appeared only the first hints of the insect transmission of disease. Sir Patrick Manson showed the mosquito carried the filaria bancrofti, and Theobald Smith demonstrated that ticks were the intermediary host in Texas fever of cattle. Finally Carlos Finlay of Havana made his famous statement that he believed that yellow fever was carried by the mosquito.

The conception of the insect as a bearer of disease brings us into the closing decade of the 19th century and the opening years of the 20th, the decade which gave us the work of Ronald Ross and Walter Reed, of Masaki Ogata, and of David Bruce, and Charles Nicolle, showing the mosquito as the carrier of malaria and of yellow fever, the tsetse fly as the fatal host of sleeping sickness, the flea that transmits bubonic plague, and the louse that carries typhus.

Perhaps nowhere is there a greater commentary on the simple practicality of modern medicine than in this field of insect-borne diseases. Six hundred years ago men believed that disease was due to the wrath of the gods; they prayed—and died. Three hundred years ago they believed it due to meteorological disturbances and contaminated air; they closed their windows at night and burned coal and powder in the streets—and died. Today we turn from such omniscient powers as the gods and the weather to prosaic matters such as exterminating of the mosquito, the killing of the rat and its fleas, and the delousing of the traveler—and we live free from plague, malaria, and yellow fever—though we have not conquered death, merely prolonged life.

Prosaic, practical are the discoveries of modern medicine—no cloud of mystery or magic obscures them; they are for every man to see and know and profit. Certainly the most striking demonstration of the indispensability of modern medical knowledge to modern engineering achievement is in the building of the Panama Canal. Yellow fever and malaria had made this district the "white man's grave." It is doubtful if the canal could have been built, and certainly it could never have been used, if medical knowledge had not shown the way to clear the land of disease. Today, under active medical control, the Canal Zone boasts of being one of the healthiest districts in the world; its borders touch upon one of the unhealthiest.

So great have been the benefits derived from the achievements of bacteriology and parasitology that the temptation is to follow on and on, telling of one after another, but in the years of the late 19th century medical science is growing in other directions, led forward by the achievements in chemistry and physics. Emil Fischer, professor at Berlin, has succeeded in synthesizing caffeine, supplied the structural formula for most of the sugars, and linked together great chains of amino acids in a protein-like structure —a presage of the work to come in the 20th century on protein deficiencies in the diet, which in time is to have a bearing upon the discovery of vitamins.

Likewise at the great school of Berlin Paul Ehrlich is speculating on the chemical theories of immunity, experimenting with dyes for the treatment of disease, and dreaming perhaps of chemical specifics to sterilize the body of parasitic bacteria and protozoa. But the realization of his dream, in part at least, comes only after the turn of the century.

But in the last decade before the opening of the new century physics makes directly two practical contributions to medicine. Marie and Pierre Curie discover radium; Wilhelm Konrad Roentgen of Wurzburg discovers the X ray. Both these contributions to basic science are seized upon for medical application. Such a movement is in the spirit of the time; it could not have occurred in the 17th or 18th century. Harvey's discovery was not seized upon and wrung dry of every practical usefulness in his time. But Roentgen's discovery was known throughout the world within a week; it was used in medicine within a month.

And now we close the 19th century, the greatest of all eras of medical progress, the period when the fundamental conceptions controlling modern medicine were formulated. We enter the 20th century, a time that engulfs our own days. Looking back from a point at which only a third of the century has passed, no one can say truly what discoveries have been made; he can point out the practical results achieved, but who knows what results? Perhaps those that will change the whole order of medicine may grow out of observations already recorded, already before us, but as yet unseen with the eye of practical application. Such has been the case in the past. Four centuries before Pasteur the doctrine of bacterial infection was formulated by Athanasius Kircher; James Lind in the 18th century held the clue to vitamin deficiency almost in his hands when he showed the efficacy of lime juice in preventing scurvy; Semmelweis's work was derisively commented on in the journals of his time, in the columns devoted to medical humor. Before eyes that are as yet blind there may be in these thirty-three years of the 20th century facts that will some day change the medicine and surgery that we know now as profoundly as

Paul Ehrlich, 1854–1915, the founder of modern chemo-therapy.

the discoveries of the 19th century changed the medicine and surgery of the 18th.

We here can record only what has been seen. Much of the progress of this century has been in the wider dissemination, in the application, the development of the revolutionary discoveries that came in the 19th century. Medical education has been greatly broadened and made more rigorous; preventive medicine has been organized, until now it has become accepted as basic necessity. Social changes are teeming with the threat of new developments in medicine, but these things are aside from our story, which is of the foundations upon which medical progress is built. So to return to the account of the known progress in the 20th century, we select only three great contributions: the control of syphilis, the rise of organotherapy, and the dietary factors in disease.

Modern Achievements

WHEN the 19th century closed, the organism of syphilis had not yet been discovered. The disease was as difficult to diagnose as it had been in the days of John Hunter; the therapy was as ineffective as it had been when that great experimentalist deliberately infected himself with the disease in an attempt to prove that gonorrhea and syphilis were different manifestations of the same disease. That false belief passed away before the pungent words of Paul Ricord and the discovery of the gonococcus by Neisser. But the therapy that John Hunter used— he died of angina—was essentially the therapy in use in the beginning of the 20th century. And then in a span of five years the whole situation changed; in that brief period there were developed the means by which this disease could be wiped out almost completely.

In 1905 Fritz Schaudinn of Germany discovered the parasite of syphilis. In 1906 August von Wassermann developed the diagnostic serum test for syphilis; in this same year Metchnikoff described a specific prophylactic measure. In 1910 Paul Ehrlich

announced the discovery of the first of the arsenicals
for the cure of syphilis—one of those rare finds in
therapy, a specific as reliable as quinine in the treatment of malaria. What the future may bring from
this field of chemical therapy—the dream of Paracelsus, the reality of Ehrlich—no one can predict.
Possibly it may take a leading rôle in the medicine of
the balance of our century.

The second great achievement of the 20th century, organotherapy, has beginnings that date back
into antiquity. But it is a long span from the ancient man who ate the heart of a lion to save him
from cowardice to the man of today who uses liver
extract to save him from pernicious anaemia, or
who takes thyroid extract to save him from myxedema, or insulin to treat his diabetes. The man who
ate the lion's heart was motivated by mystery and
magic; organotherapy as a practical treatment is a
product almost wholly of the 20th century. But for
its beginning we must seek in the 19th century
among events which we have already mentioned—
the work of Claude Bernard, of Basedow and Graves,
of Addison, and of Brown-Séquard.

The first practical results were obtained with the
thyroid gland. Throughout the latter 19th century
there grew up the belief that in some mysterious way
disturbances of the thyroid gland were associated with
disease. Experiments and surgery as well proved that
removal of the thyroid resulted in myxedema. It was
found, even, that in some cases grafting the tissue of

the thyroid into the body averted for a time, at least, the symptoms of myxedema. This observation led to the first attempt to use thyroid extract to relieve cretinism and myxedema. The iodine content of the extract was recognized, but the conception of hormone regulation of bodily function was not fully established until 1902, when Sir William Bayliss and Ernest Starling showed that the flow of pancreatic juice is initiated not by nervous control directly but by the absorption of a substance from the mucosa of the intestine secretion. From that point onward the conceptions of internal secretion grew, until now one after another of the hormones have been discovered and their function established.

Unquestionably the greatest practical result from organotherapy has been the isolation of insulin by Banting and Best. The story of their discovery commences with the observations by Claude Bernard on the glycogenic function of the liver; it concluded in the large-scale commercial manufacture of insulin; consequently in a new era for the diabetic patient. Today we have taken only our first steps in organo-therapy—no one can predict the future of this field, but it is bright with the promise of disease-control beyond the dreams even of Brown-Séquard.

We turn next to a subject close in a way to hormone action and yet one exercised mainly thru the diet—the vitamins. And as a transition from one field to the next, for it falls between the two, we pause to record that great discovery of only a few years ago,

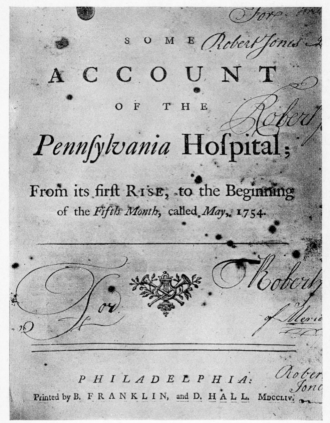

Frontispiece of a History of the Pennsylvania Hospital—printed by Benjamin Franklin.

the one which is associated with the names of Whipple and Minot and Murphy, that the once invariably fatal disease, pernicious anaemia, yields almost miraculously to liver or extract of liver or, as William Castle has now shown, to extract of the stomach mucosa.

There is in that discovery a commentary on the changing methods of the approach to medical problems. Addison contented himself with describing pernicious anaemia—the descriptive approach of the past; Whipple, and Minot, and Murphy sought ways of controlling the disease, and they used the modern or experimental approach. And it is this same approach that has yielded us our knowledge of the vitamins. There are thousands of descriptions of scurvy dating back for centuries; modern researches have replaced these graphic accounts with the knowledge of vitamin C. Descriptions of scurvy should no longer be needed, except for historic interest; in the light of modern knowledge the disease should have no existence.

The researches on vitamins, those accessory but necessary food substances that exert an almost hormone-like action in promotion of normal bodily function, are still in their infancy. As researches they are very modern, but their roots extend clear back to the empiric knowledge of those days when the American Indians showed the early settlers how to prevent scurvy with hemlock infusion and to the time when Lind and Cook introduced fruit juice and fresh vegetables into navy diet. Scurvy, which once decimated the armies and navies of the world and ravaged the crusaders, was conquered by fruit juice.

Cod-liver oil, so important in the prevention and cure of rickets and certain bone diseases of adults, has likewise its ancient history of empiric use; but its justification dates from the discovery of its active principles. The vitamins A and D belong to modern researches, as does all our other knowledge of vitamins.

The discoveries in the fields of the vitamins are well known indeed, although they are still so new that we cannot even speculate upon their eventual outcome. Nevertheless there are those that future generations, taller, stronger, more robust, and healthier than we, shall look back at and characterize as perhaps the greatest contributions of the early 20th century.

You who have read these pages, recording briefly, far too briefly, and in but fragmentary form, the triumphs of modern medicine, have seen the rise of medicine from mystery to magic and from magic to science—a science exerting today the strongest force in civilization for human betterment, a science that to those who devote to it their lives seems almost a religion, one that has as its aims a longer and healthier life, freedom from disease and suffering. And the priests of that religion are our physicians, for, although they have laid aside the mystery and turned to science, they have never yet discarded from their ethics the religious principles of sacrifice of self to others, principles older than science. The science of the laboratory we have emphasized in these pages because from it has come the science of modern medicine, but no matter how glorious are its potential benefits, how great its contributions, it is not of itself medicine complete. As long as human beings remain human beings, art as well as science, the contact of personality, must remain an integral part of the practice of medicine. It is not to the great research worker, nor yet to industry that we turn when in pain, but to the physician, the man. And the physician of today, aided by science and industry, stands, as A. Lawrence Lowell has said, "upon the prow of the ship of civilization." No longer is he scanning the horizon for the sight of sea monsters and other fabrications of mystery and magic. With chart in hand and scientific instruments of precision at his disposal he is piloting us toward the peaceful harbor of old age, undisturbed by the terrors which formerly haunted the most intrepid voyager on the sea of life.

GLOSSARY OF PROPER NAMES*
AND MEDICAL TERMS

Robert Adams (1791-1875). Famous for his classical accounts of essential heart block. His name is preserved to us in the terminology for Stokes-Adams syndrome, a condition usually occurring in partial heart block and characterized by slow pulse, vertigo, or epileptiform attacks and visible impulses in the veins of the neck. When the excitation wave from the auricles to the ventricles is completely blocked, the ventricles assume a rhythm of their own, which is, however, out of pace with that of the auricles. *102*

Thomas Addison (1793-1860). A colleague of Bright at Guy's Hospital. Although he was so little interested in prescribing that he sometimes forgot to do so, yet Addison's pill of calomel, digitalis, and squills is still used. In 1849 he read a paper before the medical society in which he described pernicious anemia, and this was later expanded into a monograph, "On the Constitutional and Local Effects of Disease of the Suprarenal Capsules," London, 1855. Although looked upon only as a scientific curiosity in his time, it is now recognized as of epoch-making importance. The disease is now known as Addison's Disease. *106*

Aesculapius. Greek God of Medicine—son of Apollo, by the Nymph Coronis. He became so proficient in the healing art, that Pluto accused him of diminishing the number of shades in Hades. He was therefore destroyed by the thunderbolt of Zeus.

The British Museum possesses a beautiful head of Aesculapius from the island of Melos. *31*

Aretaeus. Greek physician of the time of Emperor Hadrian. *34*

Leopold Auenbrugger (1722-1809). Physician in chief of the Hospital of the Holy Trinity in Vienna. He ascertained by clinical observation and by experiment on the cadaver that it was possible to obtain information about the condition of the interior of the

---

*Page numbers (italics at end of each paragraph) indicate principal reference in text.

chest by striking it gently with the points of the fingers, a method known as immediate percussion to distinguish it from mediate percussion so largely used today, where a finger or a plessimeter intervenes between the chest and the tapping finger. Auenbrugger's great discovery was slighted and neglected during his lifetime, but Auenbrugger himself was too well poised to worry about his posthumous reputation. *78*

Avicenna, "Prince of Physicians" (980-1037). It was mainly accident which caused his writings to be the guide to medical study in European universities from the twelfth to the seventeenth century, thus eclipsing the names of Rhazes and Avenzoar. *42*

Frederick Grant Banting (1891-   ). Canadian physician. Banting returned from serving in the war at Salonica and settled in Western Ontario where he had an appointment as Assistant in Physiology at the University. Without being very familiar with previous work on the hormones of the pancreas he became interested in obtaining an extract which would be suitable for the treatment of diabetes. At the end of the year he went to Professor Macleod at the University of Toronto, and begged for an opportunity to pursue the work he was doing. He had considerable difficulty in persuading the latter that he had a fruitful problem on which to work but by being persistent he got an appointment. At the end of a few months he had made such progress that he got the promise of an assistant, and the next term he was given Charles Herbert Best to help him. In the next two years they worked out the problem of Insulin and published their results in 1923, revolutionizing the treatment and the outlook of the diabetic patient. *140*

Carl Adolph v. Basedow (1799-1854). Described in 1840 three cases of the disease, exophthalmic goiter, which is also known by his name. Robert James Graves had five years earlier published such an admirable description of the disease that the symptoms resulting from increased activity of the thyroid are also called after him, Graves's Disease. *106*

William Maddock Bayliss (1860-1924). British physiologist and author of a treatise on general physiology. The greater part of Bayliss' work was done in association with Starling, and the article on Starling may be referred to for his scientific accomplishments. Bayliss was possessed of remarkable critical judgment. He was widely read and acquainted with scientific literature and found great enjoyment in the development of technical methods of research. *140*

GLOSSARY OF PROPER NAMES

William Beaumont (1785-1853). Surgeon in the U. S. Army, famous for his experiments and observations on the physiology of digestion made possible by the healing of a gunshot wound leaving an opening to the exterior. Beaumont carefully reviewed the work of his predecessors and then accurately described the phenomena taking place during digestion. He began his work at an isolated military post and continued it by bringing his patient, Alexis St. Martin, to Plattsburgh Barracks. *102*

Emil von Behring (1854-1917). German bacteriologist who commenced his career as a Prussian army surgeon. Pierre Paul Emil Roux and Alexandre Yersin, pupils of Pasteur, had, subsequent to the latter's work on chicken cholera, shown that cultures of diphtheria bacilli, from which the bacteria had been removed by filtration, likewise contained a poisonous substance which could produce all of the toxic symptoms and local reactions of the disease. Von Behring, working in Koch's Institute with Kitasato, showed that tissues acclimatized by repeated injections of such poisons produced a substance, which he called antitoxin, capable of neutralizing the toxin. This substance, at first confined to the cells, is produced in such quantity that it overflows into the blood stream, from whence it is distributed throughout the body. Von Behring, after trying out the remedy in man, began to produce the antitoxin on a grand scale in 1894, and it was immediately recognized as a specific treatment for diphtheria. *130*

Sir Charles Bell (1774-1842). Scottish anatomist. He had a very considerable practical knowledge of anatomy and great skill as an artist, publishing engravings of the brain and nervous system, and in 1811, *A New Idea of the Brain and Nervous System,* in which he announced the functions of nerves in relation to corresponding parts of the brain. He showed, among other things, that the anterior roots of the spinal nerves as they emerge from the cord are motor, while the posterior roots are sensory. He had risen to be one of the foremost scientific men in London, with a large surgical practice, when he was offered the Chair of Surgery at Edinburgh, accepting it because "London is a place to live in but not to die in." *104*

E. B. von Bergmann (1836-1907). A native of Russia who served in both the Russian and Prussian armies and was made Professor of Surgery at Würzburg and later at Berlin. He is notable for many original pieces of work besides his contributions to the advancement of cranial surgery and the treatment of head injuries. *122*

Claude Bernard (1813-1878). The greatest French physiologist.

Born on the shores of the Mediterranean, he started life as a poor boy with some literary talent and aspirations for becoming a dramatic poet. Going to Paris with his work, Saint-Marc Girardin dissuaded him from adopting literature as a profession and urged him to study medicine as a surer way of gaining a livelihood. He became an almost unapproachable master in the technique of experimental procedure, embellishing his work in addition by his literary accomplishments. At first, Claude Bernard was looked upon as a mere vivisector of animals and he states that he owes much of his immunity from persecution to friendship with a police commissioner. During the lifetime of Magendie, a special professorship in general physiology was created for him at the Sorbonne and he succeeded Magendie as full professor of physiology at the College de France. Louis Napoleon was so fascinated by his personality as to give him, after an interview, two fine laboratories, thus correcting a lack which he had long felt. Claude Bernard's greatest achievements were based upon accidentally discovered facts, facts which, through his remarkable power of thinking physiologically, he used as clues to larger results. Besides his discovery that the liver converts food substances into a sugar, glycogen, and stores it, he did important work on the digestive function of the pancreative juices and explained the vasomotor mechanism, demonstrating the presence of both vaso-dilator and vaso-constrictor fibers. *106*

Charles Herbert Best (1899-   ). Canadian physiologist. Co-discoverer with Banting of Insulin. *140*

Theodor Billroth (1829-1904). German surgeon. He was professor of surgery at Zürich and later at Vienna. He is best known for his remarkable success in operations on the gastro-intestinal tract. *122*

Hermann Boerhaave (1668-1738). Dutch physician who as professor of practical medicine introduced the modern system of clinical instruction and made Leyden the resort of pupils from every part of Europe. *78*

Eugène Bouchut (1818-1892). French physician, who introduced intubation of the larynx for croup. He also wrote a valuable history of medicine. *118*

Richard Bright (1789-1858). Physician to Guy's Hospital in London. He was the leading consultant of his day. Bright's description of essential nephritis or Bright's disease, distinguishing dropsy due to kidney disease and dropsy due to cardiac disease, was soon recognized as of immense importance in medical practice. Bright's descriptions of many morbid states are astonishing for the clearness with which they are depicted as well as for their extraordinary number. If he had given names to the conditions he described, his work would have been even more useful. *102*

Pierre Brétonneau (1771-1862). A French physician residing in Tours who located and understood the intestinal lesions of typhoid. He is principally known for his celebrated monograph on diphtheria which gave the disease its present name. Diphtheria had been well described in the second century by Aretæus under the name of Malum Egyptiacum. In the 16th, 17th, and 18th centuries, diphtheria prevailed frequently in many parts of Europe, but there was no accurate account of the infection, distinguishing it from other throat lesions, until that of Brétonneau's. *102*

François Joseph Victor Broussais (1772-1838). Born at St. Malo. After service in the army, he was appointed to the hospital of Val-de-Grace, where he began to propound his theory that disease depends always upon local irritation of some organ, as the heart, for instance, and particularly the stomach and intestines. He believed that nature had no healing power and that it was necessary to prescribe a weakening régime which consisted, among other things, in excessive bleeding. For a while his doctrines ruled French and even European practice. *101*

John Brown (1735-1788). Scottish physician who quarreled with all preceding systems of medicine and finally published his own, called the Brunonian theory of medicine, which for a time had a great vogue. *77*

Charles-Edouard Brown-Séquard (1817-1894). British physiologist. Born in Mauritius, he led a very roving existence. In America, he was appointed Professor of Physiology at Harvard. In London, he was physician to the National Hospital for the Paralyzed and Epileptic, and, in France, he succeeded Claude Bernard as Professor of Experimental Medicine. With the latter, he is the principal founder of the doctrine of internal secretions. He contributed considerably to our knowledge of animal heat and of the nervous system. *118*

David Bruce (1855-1931). In 1894 Sir David Bruce discovered that the tsetse fly disease or nagana of Zululand was due to a trypanosome. Trypanosomes are flagellate infusoria parasitic to many forms of animal life. In Central Africa large game are immune from effects of the particular organism causing nagana, but the organisms are carried from the game to horses and cattle by the bite of the tsetse fly. Man is also subject to the disease, in whom it produces "African sleeping sickness." *133*

William Burke and William Hare. They made a practice of enticing men to their lodgings and suffocating them in order to sell their bodies to a certain Dr. Knox. The discovery and arrest of these two men had much to do with the passage of the Anatomy Act, in 1832, a bill which legalized and regulated the supply of subjects for dissection and governs the practice of anatomy up to the present day. *105*

John Calvin (1509-1564). Swiss divine and reformer. Early leader of the Reform party in France. His theology was built on the foundations of the earlier Reformers, such as Luther, but his peculiar gifts of learning and style made him the exponent of the new religion. His influence on the history of Christian thought is best seen in Scotland, in Puritan England, and in the New England States. *56*

William Bosworth Castle (1897-   ). American physician. Prominent for his work in the etiology of pernicious anemia and sprue, and for parenteral liver therapy in these diseases. *142*

Catherine de' Medici (1519-1589). Queen of France and mother of three kings of France. Daughter of Lorenzo II de' Medici. She was married to Francis I through the influence of her uncle, Pope Clement VII. This strengthened the hand of Francis in his wars against Charles V. During the wars of religion the Queen sought to advance first the interests of her children and then the Catholic cause, and to this end finesse, lying, and assassination were her most effective weapons. It was she who planned the massacre of St. Bartholomew, and it was her son, the King, who saw to it expressly that Ambroise Paré, a conscientious Protestant, should be spared during the massacre. *61*

Henry Cavendish (1731-1810). English chemist and physicist, a man of extraordinary eccentricity, great timidity and reserve whose scientific work is distinguished for its range, exactness, and accuracy. He was, by inheritance, one of the richest men of his time and in spite of his reticence, acquired a very high reputation within his own country and abroad. *78*

Aurelius Cornelius Celsus. A Roman nobleman and man of letters of the time of Tiberius Caesar. He composed a series of technical works one of which upon medicine, *De re medicina,* was long a standard treatise after the close of the Middle Ages. *34*

GLOSSARY OF PROPER NAMES

Guy de Chauliac (1300-1368). A most erudite and eminent authority on surgery in the fourteenth and fifteenth centuries. *47*

Julius Cohnheim (1839-1884). A pupil of Virchow's and successively professor of pathology at Kiel, Breslau, and Leipzig. His monograph *On Inflammation and Suppuration* revolutionized pathology, showing, in direct opposition to the teaching of Virchow, that the essential feature of inflammation is the passage of white blood cells through the walls of the capillaries and that pus and pus cells are thus formed and have their origin in the blood constituents. *123*

Emperor Charles V (1500-1558). Roman Emperor and King of Spain, The Netherlands, Naples, Sicily, and Sardinia. Grandson of Ferdinand and Isabella. The Empire carried with it serious liabilities and no reliable assets and was further complicated by the growth of Lutheranism and an inherited quarrel with France. Charles did much to consolidate and make possible at a later date the independent State of the Netherlands. His reign was the age of the conquest and organization of the American possessions. *60*

André Chantemesse (1851-1919). French physician who was occupied especially with bacteriology and hygiene, his principal work being done on typhoid fever. *129*

Abraham Colles (1773-1843). Professor of Surgery in Dublin. He wrote the original description of that fracture of the wrist known as "Colles fracture" and promulgated Colles' Law relating to the supposed immunity which a healthy mother acquires in bearing a syphilitic child. *102*

Sir Dominic John Corrigan (1802-1880). A number of characteristic signs are known by his name: the Corrigan or water-hammer pulse occurring in aortic regurgitation; and the expansile pulsation of aneurism known as "Corrigan's sign." *102*

Jean-Nicolas Corvisart (1755-1821). The favorite physician of Napoleon and the teacher of Laennec. He is principally famous for his recognition of Auenbrugger's work on percussion and for his introduction of it to a general European appreciation. *79*

Carl Siegmund Franz Credé (1819-1902). Director of the obstetrical wards at the Charité in Berlin and Professor of Obstetrics at Leipzig, he introduced two extremely important measures: a method of removing the placenta by external manual expression and of preventing infantile gonorrheal conjunctivitis by the instillation of silver nitrate solution in the eyes of the newborn (1884). The latter procedure is now obligatory in most countries. *118*

The Crusades. A series of wars for delivering the Holy Land from the Mohammedans, constituting in reality a continuous flow of forces eastward and westward and forming a great epic in civilization by which the West and East were familiarized and great trade and intellectual movements initiated. *46*

Pierre (1859-1906) and Marie (1867-   ) Curie. Pierre Curie was born in Paris and educated at the Sorbonne, where he became professor of physics. In 1896 Becquerel had discovered the radioactive properties of uranium. The fact that some minerals of uranium, such as pitchblende, were more active than uranium, led Pierre Curie and his wife, Marie Sklodowska, to subject pitchblende to a laborious fractionation and, as a result, they were able in 1898 to announce the existence of two highly radioactive substances—polonium and radium. Subsequently, polonium has been shown to be a transition product of the other.

Pierre Curie was killed by a dray in Paris. Subsequently, Madame Curie was made professor at the Sorbonne and has devoted her life to research on radioactivity. *135*

Charles Robert Darwin (1809-1882). English naturalist. The whole advancement of scientific medicine in the second half of the 19th Century may be said to have resulted from the introduction of a biological or evolutionary view of processes and structures of life. From this new viewpoint arose the basic medical sciences which have made possible the medicine of today. All this was principally due to the evolutionary theories of Charles Darwin. His creative genius was inspired by a desire to build up hypotheses from whose aid further knowledge could be obtained, and it was tempered by an unbiased mind and love of truth which enabled him to modify his creations when they ceased to be supported by observations. He was particularly remarkable for the even balance between these powers of creation and judgment.

In 1831 he took the position of naturalist on the *Beagle,* a vessel starting on a surveying expedition which lasted for five years, visiting the South American Coast and the islands of the Pacific. The observations made on this voyage furnished him with abundant material concerning both living animals and fossil remains, and the next years of his life were spent in organizing it. He then devoted himself to labor on his great work, *On the Origin of Species by Means of Natural Selection or the Preservation of Favorite Races in the Struggle of Life. 119*

Charles Dickens (1812-1870). His work, *Martin Chuzzlewit,* closes his great period of character writing. **Mrs. Sairey Gamp,**

GLOSSARY OF PROPER NAMES

Mr. Pecksniff, and Mrs. Harris have passed into the national language and life of England. *116*

Sir Kenelm Digby (1603-1665). English author, diplomat, and naval officer. In addition to being greatly preoccupied with the doctrinal religious quarrels of his time, Digby was interested in politics and, to some extent, in natural science. He was a firm believer in astrology and alchemy, and readily offered evidence in proof of the sympathetic or magnetic cure of wounds. *66*

Pedacius Dioscorides. Wrote (77-78 A. D.) the greatest known work on the materia medica of ancient times. Until as late as the seventeenth century it was the most valuable guide to medicinal drugs and plants. A beautifully illustrated edition of the text is to be found in the Bibliotheque Nationale, Paris. *35*

Dorothea Lynde Dix (1802-1887). At an early age she opened a school in Boston and began teaching poor, neglected children. From time to time poor health interfered with her teaching, and she devoted her time to writing books and stories for children. Her *Conversations on Common Things* went to sixty editions before 1869. In 1841 she became interested in the conditions of jails and almshouses and particularly the pauper insane, visiting all the institutions in Massachusetts. By a memorial to the State Legislature, she was influential in providing for the proper care and treatment of the insane and gradually extended this work to all the States of the Union and to many foreign countries, France, Italy, Austria, Greece, Turkey, Russia, Norway, Sweden, Holland, Belgium, Germany, and even Japan. *95*

Henri Dunant (1828-1910). Swiss philanthropist. In 1862 he wrote a book entitled, *Un Souvenir de Solferino,* in which he described the sufferings of the wounded in the battle of Solferino so vividly that it became of general public interest. An international congress of Red Cross societies convened at Geneva in 1863, and finally an official convention was called at Geneva in 1864 by the Swiss government, and on August 26th, on behalf of the states represented, an agreement was made which eventually received the adherence of every civilized Power. There was thus put on an absolute basis the Red Cross idea, which had been loosely in force for nearly a century. For, when, on the insistence of Sir John Pringle, the Earl of Stair suggested to the Duke of Noailles that the hospitals on both sides should be considered as sanctuaries for the sick and mutually protected, the suggestion was readily agreed to by the French general. *125*

MYSTERY, MAGIC, AND MEDICINE

Guillaume Dupuytren (1777-1835). French surgeon. A poor boy, he worked his way up at the Hôtel-Dieu until he finally became head surgeon. He was remarkable for his operative skill, for his ability as a diagnostician, and as a clinical teacher. His lectures and his extensive practice soon made him the leading surgeon of France, and he died a millionaire and a baron of the Empire. As a result of his early life, he was overbearing, unscrupulous, and hard, so that he was called the "first of surgeons" and the "least of men." He is principally famous for his original descriptions of injuries and diseases of the bones, and certain other phases of surgical pathology. *101*

Paul Ehrlich (1854-1915). German pathologist. Early in his student days, became interested in experiments with dye-stuffs and the staining of tissues. He was the great pioneer in the micro-chemical reactions of tissues to dye-stuffs. From this he developed the famous "side chain" theory which considers the living protoplasmic molecule to consist of a stable nucleus and certain receptors which enable it to combine with various substances, among which may be mentioned toxins or other poisons. Von Wassermann states that without that theory he could not have hit upon his method of diagnosis for syphilis.

Ehrlich next turned his attention to the treatment of protozoan diseases by the use of synthetized coal-tar derivatives. As the outcome of this work he developed "606" and "914," now known respectively as Arsphenamine and Neoarsphenamine, substances invaluable in the treatment of syphilis and ideal for the treatment of certain other trypanozome diseases, such as yaws. Ehrlich's work marks the beginning of the recent trend of medicine from bacterial to bio-chemical investigation. *138*

Bartolommeo Eustachi (1500-1574). Professor in the Collegia della Sapienza in Rome. His anatomical engravings were executed in 1552, but were not published until 1714 (by G. M. Lancisi, physician to Pope Clement XI). He described the minute structures of many organs. The eustachian tube, connecting the inner ear with the nasal cavity, bears his name. *60*

Wilhelm Fabry (1560-1624). Also called Fabricius Hildanus. A conservative but bold and skilful operator whose *Century of Surgical Cases* is the best collection of the time. *74*

Gabriel Daniel Fahrenheit (1686-1736). German physicist who lived in England and Holland and made a living by the manufacture of meteorological instruments. He introduced important improvements in the construction of thermometers and the scale known by his name is still extensively used in Great Britain and the United States for the measurement of temperatures. *78*

Gabriello Fallopius (1523-1562). Italian anatomist. Professor of surgery, anatomy, and botany at the University of Padua, and superintendent of the botanical garden. In his *Observations Anatomicæ* (Venice, 1561), he describes the uterus with its appendages, the Fallopian tubes. *60*

Carlos Juan Finlay (1833-1915) (see article on **Walter Reed**). *133*

Emil Fischer (1852-1919). He was successively professor of chemistry at Munich, Erlangen, Würzburg, and finally at Berlin. He devoted himself to organic chemistry, in which he showed an originality of idea and resourcefulness which made him the master of this branch of experimental chemistry. No substance seemed too complex to admit of analysis or synthesis; the more difficult the problem the more conspicuous his skill in solving it. His first great work consisted in showing the relationship of the many compounds in the purin group. He next studied the sugars, substances extremely complex and difficult to get into manageable form. He synthesized many of them and then turned to study the ferments and enzymes which bring about their decomposition. From this subject he went to a still more complex problem, namely, the proteins. The tremendous merit of his researches has been recognized by all the important scientific societies in the world, and his laboratory at Berlin became one of the most important in existence. *135*

Benjamin Franklin (1706-1790). American statesman and scientist. Beginning life as a printer, he had remarkable success in this capacity and as a journalist. A citizen of Philadelphia, he was the guiding force in almost every measure or project for the welfare and prosperity of the city, and was principally instrumental in the founding of the Pennsylvania Hospital. Given the task of representing Colonial interests abroad, his foreign commissions were executed with what must be regarded as conspicuous success. During his foreign residency he made many and valuable friends. When examined by the House of Parliament in Committee of the Whole on the effects of the Stamp Act, he is said by Burke to have reminded him of a master examined by a parcel of school boys. When he was chosen, in 1776, Commissioner to France for the Colonies, he was a member of every important scientific society in Europe and one of the most talked about men in the world. His reputation was greater than that of Leibnitz, Newton, and Voltaire and he was more beloved and esteemed than any of them. So many medallions of him were in circulation that he would have been recognized in any part of the civilized world. *78*

Girolamo Frascastoro (1483-1553). Physician and poet. Among other accomplishments, with Leonardo da Vinci, he recognized fossils as the remains of animals once capable of living in the locality. *64*

Frederick II known as Frederick the Great (1712-1786). King of Prussia. By great energy and the judicious use of his resources, he raised the position of his State to one of the first rank in Europe. *43*

Robert Fulton (1765-1818). American engineer interested in experiments with submarine explosives and in steam navigation. He had more success in introducing the latter than the former and with Robert R. Livingston obtained exclusive right to navigate the waters of New York State with steam vessels. The first vessel, the *Clermont,* had an engine made by Boulton and Watt. They operated the first practical ferry between New York and Brooklyn, with great financial advantage to their enterprise. *78*

Claudius Galen (130-201 A. D.). Called Gallien by Chaucer. The most versatile, accomplished, and celebrated of ancient medical writers. He possessed even in his own time an enormous reputation as a physician. *36*

Galileo Galilei (1564-1642). Italian astronomer. While watching a lamp swinging in the Cathedral of Pisa he observed that no matter how far it swung the excursion was always executed in the same time. He later used this fact for the construction of an astronomical clock. When professor of mathematics at Padua, his lectures were attended by persons of the highest distinction from all parts of Europe, and a hall capable of containing two thousand people had eventually to be assigned for the accommodation of his audiences. Although not the inventor of the telescope, he succeeded in producing an instrument of which the present-day example is embodied in the ordinary opera glass, and thus founded a new era in the history of astronomy. His researches with the telescope were rewarded by the Venetian Senate with the appointment for life of a professorship at an unprecedentedly high salary.

Although he did not raise the theological issue of the discrepancy between the Copernican theory of the universe and passages in the Scripture, he was impetuous in the discussion of the subject. Galileo's life spanned the interval between the death of Michael Angelo and the birth of Isaac Newton. His genius is attested by the ability with which he correctly interpreted many phenomena whose true significance has only been thoroughly understood since the availability of modern instruments. *56*

Luigi Galvani (1737-1798). Italian physiologist noted for his experiments on the contraction of muscles, when electrically stimulated. He also noticed that the same effect could be obtained by a conductor composed of two dissimilar metals, but it was Volta who recognized that this metallic junction was the source of the current. *78*

Vasco da Gama (1460-1524). Portuguese navigator who rounded the southernmost tip of Africa in 1497, thus discovering the sea route to India. The Portuguese voyages, discoveries, and colonizations in India have been described in one of the most noteworthy epic poems of all times, "The Lusiads," by Camoëns. *48*

Manual Garcia (1805-1906). A Spanish singing teacher in London, who, in 1855, invented the modern laryngoscope and sent an account of his instrument to the Royal Society. This instrumental method soon became a permanent feature of this branch.of medicine. *119*

Fielding Garrison (1870-   ). Lieutenant Colonel, Medical Corps, U. S. Army. Has devoted many years to the development of the Surgeon General's Library. He is the author of the *An Introduction to History of Medicine,* one of the best books of its kind. *88*

William Wood Gerhard (1809-1872). A Philadelphian, educated in Paris under the famous French physician Pierre Louis who gave typhoid fever its present name. Gerhard was physician to the Pennsylvania Hospital, and he is principally famous as being the first definitely to separate typhus and typhoid fevers. *102*

Saint-Marc Girardin (1801-1873). French politician and man of letters, who began in 1828 to contribute to the *Journal des Débats* and continued for nearly half a century. He was appointed by Louis Philippe Professor of History and, later, Professor of Poetry at the Sorbonne, where he published his work on the usage of the of the passions in the drama. *106*

Albrecht von Graefe (1828-1870). Greatest of all eye surgeons and, with Helmholtz and Donders, the creator of modern ophthalmology. In 1854, he founded the *Archiv für Ophthalmologie,* which has continued to the present time to be the most important journal for this branch of medicine. All of the great ophthalmologists of the nineteenth century were pupils of von Graefe. *118*

Johann Gutenberg (1398-1468). A native of Mainz, Germany. Began some time after 1450, with eight hundred gilders and other moneys loaned by Johann Fust at Strassburg, the printing of a large folio Latin Bible—1282 printed pages of two columns, forty-two lines each. The first copy was discovered in the Library of Cardinal Mazarin. Sir John Thorold's copy of the Gutenberg Bible fetched in 1844 $19,500. *50*

Stephen Hales (1677-1761). English physiologist and chemist known for his experiments in plant physiology and on the rate of flow and force of the blood, etc. His apparatus or ventilator for introducing fresh air into jails, hospitals, and ships reduced the mortality in the Savoy prison. *78*

Albrecht von Haller (1708-1777). Swiss physiologist. One of the most imposing figures in medicine after Galen, Haller was an infant prodigy. At the age of four he read and expounded the Bible, at ten he had written a Chaldee grammar and a Greek and Hebrew vocabulary. While still a sickly and shy youth he went at the age of sixteen to the University of Tübingen to study medicine and then to Leyden. His botanical and anatomical researches, made during the early period when he was practicing medicine, procured for him a European reputation and the Chair of Medicine, Anatomy, Botany and Surgery at the University of Göttingen, subjects in which, except for surgery, he was equally eminent. He also founded, in a way, the science of medical and scientific bibliography. *77*

William Stewart Halsted (1852-1922). Professor of surgery at the Johns Hopkins University and Chief Surgeon of Johns Hopkins Hospital from the time of its opening until his death. He was a pioneer in America in introducing the scientific method for the improvement of surgical technique. Nowhere have serious operations been more carefully and thoroughly conceived and performed, and there has never been a clinic in which the delicate art of the perfect healing of wounds was better demonstrated. *122*

Code of Hammurabi (also known as the Laws of Khammurabi, first King of the "First Dynasty of Babylon" 2285-2242 B. C.). This is the oldest extant criminal code. It contains definite schemes and scales of offenses and punishments and indicates the existence of tribunals to try the offenses and to award the appropriate remedy. The code established physicians' fees. A copy of the code is in the Louvre, Paris. *16*

Sir John Harington (1516-1612). English writer. Godson of Queen Elizabeth, his talents made him a successful courtier. His writings were of a Pantagruelistic nature but withal smart and witty. *44*

Harun al-Rashid (763-809). Fifth of the Abbasid Caliphs of Bagdad. Many learned men enjoyed his patronage. He and Charlemagne exchanged gifts and compliments as masters respectively of the East and West. *40*

William Harvey (1578-1657). Discoverer of the circulation of the blood, which discovery was the most momentous event in medical history since the time of Galen. Graduated from Padua at twenty-four, sixteen years later he was appointed Physician Extraordinary to James I and later to Charles I. It is necessary in estimating the character of Harvey's discovery, and what is more important, its mathematical demonstration, to bear in mind that Aristotle and his successors taught that the blood is carried from the heart by means of the veins and that the arteries carry a sort of air. Although Galen had discovered that the arteries contained blood and were not merely air pipes, as their name implies, there was no conception of a continuous stream returning to its source. The movement of the blood was, on the contrary, thought to be slow and irregular in direction. *66*

Hermann Ludwig Ferdinand von Helmholtz (1821-1894). German philosopher and scientist and incidentally perhaps the greatest ophthalmologist of all time. He early showed great mathematical powers, but because of the poverty of his family, he could not follow a scientific career and, therefore, became a surgeon in the Prussian army. In 1847, while living in the barracks at Potsdam, he wrote a paper on the conservation of force, which made him one of the founders of the now universally-accepted Law of the Conservation of Energy. This paper immediately established his reputation and in 1849 he was appointed Professor of Physiology and Pathology at Königsberg, then of Anatomy and Physiology at Bonn, then of Physiology at Heidelberg, and finally of Physics at Berlin to which was added the position of Director of the Physico-Technical Institute at Charlottenburg. His investigations occupied the whole field of science, including physiology, physiological optics, acoustics, chemistry, mathematics, electricity and magnetism, meteorology and mechanics. In 1851, he invented the ophthalmoscope by which we are enabled to view the interior of the eye. He explained the mechanism of accommodation. His great work on *Physiological Optics,* in recent years brought up to date by prominent ophthalmologists throughout the world, is by far the most important book that has ever appeared on this subject. His work on the sensations of tone makes the foundation for the science of physiological acoustics. He was equally great as a mathematician and a physicist. *119*

Hippocrates (Father of Medicine) (460-370 B. C.). Born in Cos, in the first year of the Eightieth Olympiad. A member of the family of the Asclepiadae. The best edition of his works is that of Littré, *Œuvres complètes d'Hippocrate*. Hippocrates was a contemporary of Sophocles and Euripides, Aristophanes and Pindar, Socrates and Plato, Herodotus and Thucydides, Phidias and Polygnotus. Never before, or since, have so many geniuses appeared within the same narrow limits of space and time. Laennec states that he is indebted to Hippocrates for the idea which suggested the practice of ausculta-tion, and we have the same legacy in "Hippocratic succussion." *30*

William Hogarth (1697-1764). English painter and pictorial satirist who, in the latter capacity, has never been equaled. His work is both realistic and dramatic and employs both fancy and genuine decoration in the exposal of folly and wickedness. As such he takes his place with the great masters of literature. Among his principal works may be mentioned: *The Harlot's Progress,* "A Rake's Progress," and "Marriage à la Mode." *92*

Oliver Wendell Holmes (1809-1894). American writer and physi-cian. His medical essays, among which was the one on the *Con-tagiousness of Puerperal Fever,* contain some of his shrewdest ob-servations and most sparkling wit. He was appointed in 1847 Professor of Anatomy and Physiology at Harvard University. In 1857, at the instigation of James Russell Lowell, he helped in the editing of the newly established *Atlantic Monthly,* in each number of which appeared *The Autocrat of the Breakfast Table.* The magazine would have failed in the panic of '57, had it not been for the fascination of these essays. Thus, Dr. Holmes made the *Atlantic Monthly* and the *Monthly* made him. *113*

Robert Hooke (1635-1703). A man who originated and antici-pated an understanding of many phenomena to be discovered later, but who perfected very little. His life was embittered by a morbid jealousy concerning the anticipation of his discoveries. Among his achievements may be mentioned the formulation of the undulatory theory of light, the observation of the phenomena of diffraction, universal gravitation, the use of the pendulum as a measure of gravity, spiral springs for balance wheels of watches, telescopic gun sights, etc. *72*

Hôtel-Dieu. Founded in the middle of the 7th Century by St. Landry, Bishop of Paris. It is one of the oldest and most inter-esting, as well as one of the largest, hospitals in Europe, and has always been an institution where the resident physician could obtain invaluable training. *62*

GLOSSARY OF PROPER NAMES

John Hunter (1728-1793). British physiologist and surgeon. His instincts would not permit him to "stuff Latin and Greek at the university." He was the founder of modern experimental and surgical pathology and created for the surgeon that position which made him for the first time a "gentleman." He had a tremendous influence, not only through his own works, but through a considerable number of unusually famous pupils. Kindly and generous, but outwardly rude and repellent, and often restless and quarrelsome, a victim of angina pectoris, he died as he had predicted, "at the hands of any rascal who chooses to annoy and tease me." *80*

William Hunter (1718-1783). The first great teacher of anatomy in England and elder brother of the still more famous John Hunter. He early became renowned for his private lectures and eventually was the leading obstetrician of London. He spent thirty years on his atlas of the pregnant uterus illustrated by Riemsdijk at great expense to the author. His discoveries thus presented constitute the foundation for the modern knowledge of placental anatomy. *82*

Edward Jenner (1749-1823). English physician and discoverer of vaccination. In his twenty-first year he became a favorite pupil of John Hunter with whom he resided for two years, during which time he was also employed to arrange the zoölogical specimens brought back by Captain Cook from his first voyage. He declined advantageous offers, preferring a practice in his native town. The discovery associated with his name developed gradually in his mind. His attention had been early directed to relations between cowpox and smallpox and the popular belief in the antagonism between these diseases. He mentioned this repeatedly to John Hunter who, however, was not so strongly persuaded as Jenner as to its possible importance. Locally, medical men took no notice of it or at least felt the belief to be an incorrect deduction. Five years elapsed before he succeeded in unraveling the difficulties surrounding an understanding of the problem. Finally he was able to inoculate James Phipps with matter from cowpox vesicles on the hand of Sarah Nelmes. Subsequently, when inoculated with smallpox the boy did not contract the disease. In 1798 he was able to repeat his experiments and prepared his pamphlet, which, before publishing, he took to London to demonstrate the truth of it. No one would submit to be vaccinated, but finally a surgeon inoculated a diseased child and afterwards found the patient incapable of contracting smallpox. Gradually, in spite of much opposition, the practice spread over England, principally by non-professional means. Concurrently, rapid progress had been made in the United States and on the Continent. Spain sent out an expedition to diffuse the method among her possessions. Clergymen urged vaccination upon their parishioners, the birthdays of Jenner and even the anniversary of Phipps' inoculation were celebrated as national feasts and the Empress of Russia caused the first child vaccinated to be educated at the public expense. Parliament granted Jenner a vote of ten thousand pounds and later an additional grant of twenty thousand pounds was made. He was elected a member of the chief scientific societies on the Continent and Napoleon released English prisoners when the name of Jenner was mentioned to him. Persons leaving England even obtained certificates from Jenner which served as passports. 83

Immanuel Kant (1724-1804). German philosopher whose grandfather emigrated from Scotland. For a long period he taught at the University of Königsberg in minor positions, steadily refusing appointments elsewhere. Finally, in 1770, he obtained the Chair of Logic and Metaphysics at Königsberg and eleven years later published the *Critique of Pure Reason,* a work toward which he had been steadily advancing. Within a few years this work was expounded in all the leading universities, even in the schools of the Church of Rome. Kant's work closed the lines of speculation previously current and substituted for them a comprehensive method of regarding the essential problem of thought, a method which has dominated the course of philosophical speculation to the present day. 77

Johann Kepler (1571-1630). German astronomer who by virtue of family misfortunes and feeble constitution was started on a theological vocation. A brilliant examination for the bachelor's degree procured him a place at the University of Tübingen. From there he was appointed to the Chair of Science at the University of Gratz, where certain of his duties were of an astronomical nature. He was early convinced that the actual disposition of the solar system must obey some more abstract and intelligible laws than those ascribed to it by Ptolemy. The affairs of the university having become difficult, it was through correspondence with Tycho Brahe and with Galileo that his embarrassment was relieved by his being made assistant to Tycho Brahe at the Observatory at Prague. The unexpected death of Tycho Brahe opened to Kepler the opportunity to develop his talents. It was he who developed two of the cardinal principles of modern astronomy: the laws of elliptical orbits of the heavenly bodies and of their velocity being such as to sweep out equal areas in equal times. His clear recognition of these principles and of the sun as the moving power of the solar system entitles him to rank as the founder of physical astronomy. *66*

Athanasius Kircher (1601-1680). German mathematician. He became professor of philosophy, mathematics and Oriental languages at Würzburg, whence he was driven to Avignon by the troubles of the Thirty Years' War. He subsequently taught mathematics in Rome at the Collegio Romano. He was much interested in antiquities and bequeathed a valuable collection to the college. While in Rome he devised experiments on the nature of putrefaction and believed that he had seen micro-organisms in the putrefying matter. He was the first to point to the cause of infectious diseases as a living contagion. *72*

Shibasaburo Kitasato (1856-1931). He studied medicine in Germany under Koch and became one of the foremost bacteriologists of the world. With Von Behring, he was the discoverer of antitoxin for diphtheria, and he is credited with the discovery of the bacilli of tetanus, diphtheria, and the plague. With Masaki Ogata he has done a great deal to advance the science of bacteriology in Japan. In 1892 he founded the governmental institute for infectious diseases, and later, in 1914, the Kitasato Institut.

Robert Koch (1843-1910). After serving in the Franco-Prussian War, he practised as a physician in a country district, where he began the bacteriological researches which were to make him famous. By 1880 he had published his memoirs on the anthrax bacillus, his method of staining bacteria for microscopic examination, and a paper on the etiology of traumatic infectious diseases. He was appointed a member of the Sanitary Commission in Berlin. He developed a process of steam sterilization, and while head of the German Cholera Commission, discovered the cause of the disease and the means of its transmission. In 1891 he founded the Institute for Infectious Diseases in Berlin. Koch's work entitles him to a place as one of the greatest bacteriologists ever known. *127*

René Théophile Hyacinthe Laennec (1781-1826). The inventor of the most important instrument and method of medical investigation—the stethoscope. Laennec was born in Quimper, Brittany, and was a regimental surgeon in the Revolution. He later became physician to the Hôpital Beaujon and to the Hôpital Neckar. A very modest individual, he was greatly interested in his proficiency in horseback riding. He had much better success with the introduc-

tion of his methods than Auenbrugger, for his treatise was immediately taken up and translated everywhere, thus bringing about a
revolution in the knowledge of the diseases of the chest. He
studied morbid anatomy so minutely and correlated it so carefully
with the appearance of symptoms during life that even if he had
not discovered auscultation and described the character of the sounds
which could be heard over different pathological conditions, he would
still have been famous. His descriptions of many diseased conditions are classical, and he was one of the greatest teachers on pul-
monary tuberculosis, a disease from which he died. *104*

Joseph Louis Lagrange (1736-1813). French mathematician whose
wealthy father, by good luck, lost his fortune in speculation, thus
providing Lagrange with the impetus to work. Lagrange is generally known as the founder of the calculus of variations, the most
powerful instrument which has ever been devised for the investigation of natural phenomena, and indeed it is to Lagrange that we
are indebted, more than to any other human being, for the intellectual machinery which made possible the development of the
physical equipment which characterizes modern civilization. At
nineteen he had already developed the calculus and at twenty-six
he was at the summit of European fame, his presence being sought
after as an embellishment to the principal courts of Europe. The
especial favorite of Frederick the Great and later of Marie An-
toinette, he remained, full of curiosity, to watch the French Revolution and saw many of his associates guillotined. He himself, however, was treated by the National Assembly with great respect and
headed those intellectual commissions created by the Revolutionists
for the express purpose of increasing the renown of France in all
domains of thought. It was Lagrange's advocacy of the decimal
system which was largely responsible for its adoption and he was
influential in the publication of several monumental works by the
Academical Commission. With the passing of the Revolutionists,
Napoleon loaded him with personal favors and official distinctions.
He became a senator, a Count of the Empire, and a Grand Officer
of the Legion of Honor. Lagrange was conspicuous for his work in
the advancement of almost every branch of pure mathematics. He
made possible the verification of Newton's work and was responsible for imparting a character of generality, completeness, clearness,
elegance and simplicity to the entire branch of knowledge which
concerns the investigation of the properties of matter. *78*

Jean Baptiste Octave Landry (1826-1865). He first described in
1859 an acute form of ascending paralysis of the spinal cord

which is still recognized as a clinical entity. It is a disease which, for the most part, attacks healthy young adults and is usually rapidly fatal. *118*

Pierre Simon Laplace (1749-1827). French mathematician and astronomer. His analytical investigation of the motions and perturbations of the bodies constituting the solar system was the most important step in establishing the stability of the system. He made use to an unusual degree of the intellectual machinery developed by Lagrange. His career was one of uninterrupted prosperity. With Lagrange he took part in many of the intellectual activities inspired by the Revolution. Laplace was a great and successful mathematician through the combination of an unusually original mind, a rare sagacity in detecting new truths and an enthusiasm for his work which enabled him to hold fast year after year until the answer was obtained. *78*

Alphonse Laveran (1845-1922). As an army surgeon in Algeria, he discovered in 1880 the parasites of malarial fever, and described the various forms the parasite may take on, both sexual and asexual, when the blood of man is infected by the bite of the mosquito. *133*

Antoine Laurent Lavoisier (1743-1794). French chemist. Lavoisier's name is associated with the establishment of the foundations on which the modern science of chemistry rests. The spread of his doctrine and the overthrow of the old phlogistical theory were greatly facilitated by the logical form in which he presented his facts. Lavoisier was prominent in the introduction of scientific, political, and agricultural reforms and the improvement of the social and economic conditions of the people. By this work he became connected with the farmers-general and when this body came under the suspicion of the Revolutionary authorities his fate was sealed. He was even accused by Marat of stopping the circulation of air in the city of Paris and with twenty-seven others, in 1794, was condemned to death and guillotined. Lagrange remarked that it only took them one moment to get rid of the head which one hundred years would not suffice to reproduce. *78*

Anton van Leeuwenhoek (1632-1723). Dutch microscopist. He devoted his life to the manufacture of microscopes and the study of the minute structure of animal life. He made 112 contributions to the *Philosophical Transactions of the Royal Society,* and 26 to the *Memoirs of the Paris Academy of Sciences.* From his descriptions of objects observed, his microscopes must have been of very high quality. *72*

MYSTERY, MAGIC, AND MEDICINE

Gottfried Wilhelm Leibnitz (1646-1716). German philosopher and mathematician who during the greater part of his life held political connections which placed him in active contact with affairs of State and brought him a number of honors, among which was his creation as a Baron of the Empire. Leibnitz's acquaintances comprised many notable names, among them René Descartes, Christian Huygens, Jacques Bénigne Bossuet, and Cristoval Rojas de Spinola. The philosophy of Leibnitz dominated German thought for nearly a century and to a large extent determined the character of the critical philosophy by which, almost a century later, it was superseded. *77*

Leonardo Da Vinci (1452-1519). Greatest of Italian painters, sculptor, architect, anatomist, musician, engineer, and natural philosopher. Son of a Florentine lawyer. Born out of wedlock by a mother of humble station, his mother subsequently married Ser Piero, and the son, thus brought up, possessed not only a splendid beauty, but an activity and charm of temper and manners, an aptitude for all accomplishments, and an almost inexhaustible intellectual energy. He subsequently received the special favor of Lorenzo the Magnificent. No man has ever been gifted in the same degree at once in art and in science. In the latter, he worked wholly for the future and in great part alone. In spite of the tremendous heritage which he left, no imaginable strength of any single man could suffice to carry out a one-hundredth part of what he essayed to do. *50*

Thomas Linacre (1460-1524). A native of Canterbury. In Bologna he became a pupil of Angelo Poliziano and shared the instruction given by that scholar to the sons of Lorenzo de' Medici, the Magnificent. On the accession of Henry the Eighth he was appointed the King's physician, an office of considerable influence and importance. He was chiefly instrumental in founding the Royal College of Physicians. *51*

James Lind (1716-1794). Surgeon in the Royal Navy, Lind became physician to the Royal Naval Hospital at Haslar shortly after its foundation. He is the founder of naval hygiene in England and wrote three epoch-making treatises, one on scurvy (1754), one on naval hygiene (1757) and one on tropical medicine (1758). For scurvy Lind recommended the use of fresh lemons, limes and oranges and even the preserved juice. *142*

Joseph Lister (1827-1912). England's greatest surgeon. When Lister was appointed to the Chair of Surgery at Glasgow, the general introduction of anesthetics had relieved the sufferer of his

GLOSSARY OF PROPER NAMES

agony, but the direct healing of surgical wounds was altogether a rare and singular circumstance and the mortality from infection was ghastly in the extreme. Patients dreaded the hospital and surgeons distrusted themselves, so much so that the hospital system itself was in danger of passing out of society. It was Lister who corrected all this, and who recognized that speculation as to the cause of sepsis was on the wrong tack. More than any other person, he is responsible for "opening the gates of mercy to mankind." Pasteur was already at work in unraveling the secret of bacterial life. Lister concluded that infection in wounds was analogous to putrefaction in wines, and he applied to the wound and to the operative surroundings antiseptics to destroy the infection. Although the aseptic technique has long since superseded the antiseptic method of Lister, it was in the World War, where asepsis was no longer possible, that the method first introduced by Lister was finally vindicated. In a way, Lister is comparable to Halsted in that he consistently labored and experimented to make the recovery of patients a mathematical certainty. *121*

Crawford Williamson Long (1815-1878). As a country physician of Georgia, he had noted some accidental anesthetic effects of ether and undoubtedly used ether for anesthesia in 1842 and 1843. He, however, did not publish his work until long after ether had become generally introduced through the efforts of Morton and the men at the Massachusetts General Hospital. *109*

Pierre Charles Alexandre Louis (1787-1872). French physician who overthrew the system of Broussais, particularly stopping the abuse of blood-letting in pneumonia by showing statistically that it was of little value. This method was later used for demonstrating the syphilitic origin of tabes and paresis. Louis was the first to use the watch in timing the pulse, and through his American pupils, Holmes, Jackson, and others, he exerted a powerful influence on the advancement of medical science in the United States. *104*

Abbott Lawrence Lowell (1856-   ). American educationalist. He practiced law until 1897 when he became lecturer and professor of government at Harvard. In 1909, he succeeded Eliot as president of the University from which position he resigned in 1933. *144*

Carl Friedrich Wilhelm Ludwig (1816-1895). German physiologist. He played a prominent part in the change to the modern methods of physiology which commenced about the middle of the 19th Century, explaining physiological phenomena as resulting from the operation of general physical and chemical laws rather than from special biological laws and vital forces. Through his discoveries, his method, and the apparatus which he introduced, he had a tremendous influence on the progress of physiology. But, more than this, he was perhaps the greatest teacher of physiology who ever lived. Most of Ludwig's researches were published under the names of his pupils. Von Kries says, however, that they often merely sat on the window sill while Ludwig and his assistant did all the work. Ludwig was entirely free from selfish aims and ambitions, and scrupulously conscientious in all that he said and did, but nevertheless captivating through his warmth of heart and enchanting personality. *119*

François Magendie (1783-1855). French physiologist who sought to advance physiology by a closer inspection and revision of the facts to be observed, and who regarded medicine as a science in the making. He was the first of an illustrious line of laboratory experimenters, but he himself discovered only isolated facts without trying to correlate them and so arrive at useful generalizations. *106*

Marcello Malpighi (1628-1694). Italian physiologist who was appointed in 1666 to the Chair of Theoretical Medicine at Pisa. Malpighi's discoveries in the structure of animal and vegetable matter were so important that he may be considered as the founder of microscopic anatomy. *73*

Sir Patrick Manson (1844-1922). For many years he was connected with the Chinese Imperial Maritime Customs Service. He discovered and described the organisms causing many tropical diseases. He showed that the Culex mosquito transmitted the *Filaria Bancrofti,* and that it was the cause of the tropical disease, elephantiasis. In 1886 he started a school of tropical medicine in Hongkong, and in 1898, the London School of Tropical Medicine. *133*

Sally Mapp. A bone setter and female impostor who was very successful. *92*

Cotton Mather (1663-1728). American Congregational clergyman who at one time studied medicine and wrote "An Account of the Method and Further Success of Inoculating for the Small Pox in London" (1721). Cotton Mather became one of the most influential men in the colonies. His sermons and writings did much to increase the excitement of the people against witchcraft and to influence the magistry so that when persecution ceased, liberal men everywhere turned against him. The old theocracy for which he worked was being displaced by Liberalism even before he died. *83*

John Mayow (1643-1679). English chemist and physiologist. He accepted as proved Boyle's experiment that air is necessary for combustion, but in addition he found that fire is supported, not by air as a whole, but by a "more active and subtle part of it." He rightly understood that the purpose of breathing is not to cool the heart, but that it is a mechanism for introducing oxygen into the body where it is used for the production of heat and muscular energy. *73*

Ephraim McDowell (1771-1830). A pupil of John Bell of Edinburgh, who settled in Kentucky and practised surgery with remarkable success. He was the first to perform the operation of ovariectomy, doing it thirteen times. *102*

Gregor Mendel (1822-1884). Abbot of Brünn. He published in 1865 an account of his experiments in the hybridization of peas. His method of investigation differed from that of previous ones in paying attention, while studying inheritance, to a single pair of alternative characters at a time. Thus, when crossing tall and dwarf peas, he found that the hybrids or first generation were all tall. Therefore tallness was the dominant characteristic. The next generation was composed of three talls to one dwarf. Of these, one of the talls and the dwarf always bred true. The other two talls always gave, as did the original hybrids, three talls to one dwarf. If we represent the two characteristics by the letters a and b, the law may be explained in the form of Newton's binomial theorem:

$$(a + b)^2 = a^2 + 2ab + b^2$$

If a is the dominant characteristic—the tall pea, for instance—then the a^2 and the $2ab$ are both tall, and the a^2 and b^2 will both breed true. *124*

Friedrich Anton Mesmer (1733-1815). Austrian physician who was interested in astrology. He imagined that the stars exerted an influence on human beings by means of animal magnetism. On moving to Paris, he for a short time created great excitement by the marvelous effects of mesmerism. In his dimly lighted consulting rooms hung with mirrors, patients joined hands around a vat in which chemicals were concocted, while Mesmer, dressed as a magician, passed among them, affecting them by a touch or a look. Franklin and Baillie were members of a commission appointed by the government to investigate him. *92*

Elie Metchnikoff (1845-1916). Russian biologist who showed that cells capable of amœboid movement, arising either from the connective tissue or from the white blood cells, have the power to engulf solid particles and bacteria, destroying the latter by absorbing them. He demonstrated the functions of these phagocytes as scavengers. His best work has thus to do with comparative pathology of inflammation. He is also well known for his theory concerning the value of lactic acid producing bacteria in counteracting intestinal poisons and prolonging life. *132*

George Richards Minot (1885-   ). American pathologist and physician. Prominent for his work on diseases of the blood and particularly for the discovery that liver may be used for the successful treatment of pernicious anemia. *141*

Silas Weir Mitchell (1829-1914). Leading American neurologist of his time, he had studied in Paris and been a pupil of Claude Bernard's. In medicine he is remembered for his Rest Cure, his ideas on the subject being summed up in a monograph, *Fat and Blood,* published in 1877. He studied the effect of meteorological changes on traumatic neuralgias, particularly in old amputation stumps. Mitchell ranks with Goldsmith and Holmes as a poet and novelist. He represented by his person and manner the old-fashioned American gentleman of the Colonial type, resembling some of the great 18th-Century physicians. *126*

Jean Baptiste Poquelin (Molière) (1622-1673). The greatest of French dramatists. The reason why Molière was substituted for his family name is unknown. He belonged to a family of prosperous tradesmen. He early renounced his position as a "valet de chambre du roi" and undertook the management of a company calling themselves the L'Illustre Théâtre which hired tennis courts and gave dramatic performances. Even though he received a present of the cast-off wardrobe of the duc de Guise, this was not enough to make his performances successful, and he was actually arrested by tradesmen seeking to collect their debts.

After spending much time with the same venture in the Provinces, he finally had an opportunity to play one of Corneille's pieces before King Louis XIV. This was practically a failure, but Molière came forward and asked permission to act one of his little pieces, the *Docteur amoureux,* which surprised and pleased the audience, and started him on a successful career.

Molière was remarkable for his gentleness, generosity and delicacy. Within the limits of social and refined comedy, he was probably the greatest of all writers, his humor showing the value of a true sense of life, enlivened by the most vivacious wit and the keenest observation. He is the greatest man of literary France, and in modern drama, is second only to Shakespeare. To this he combined an unerring knowledge of the theatre and the genius of a great actor and a great manager.

In the later years of his life, Molière's health was impaired and he was probably obliged to consult pedantic physicians of an age when medicine was still a matter of tradition and superstition. Several of his pieces not only ridicule the medicine of his time, but give a charming picture of the weaknesses of both the doctor and the patient. *74*

Henri de Mondeville (1260-1320). His surgical treatise shows great common sense concerning the aseptic treatment of wounds and is in opposition to the salve surgery of the Galenists. He said, "God did not exhaust all his creative power in making Galen." *46*

Mary Wortley Montagu (1689-1762). She eloped with Edward Wortley Montagu, a brother of one of her close friends and a member of Parliament for Westminster. In 1618 he was appointed ambassador to Constantinople and Lady Mary accompanied him. Her observations of Eastern life are told in a series of lively letters. From Turkey she brought back the practice of inoculation for smallpox, a practice which was later to be superseded by the much safer vaccination of Jenner. *83*

Anne, Duc de Montmorency (1493-1567). Belonging to one of the oldest and most distinguished families in France, from which have come six constables and twelve marshals of France besides admirals, cardinals, and grand officers of the crown, he distinguished himself as a commander in the wars against Charles V. *62*

University of Montpellier. First founded about 738. It exerted tremendous influence on medicine throughout the Middle Ages. *46*

Giovanni Battista Morgagni (1682-1741). Italian anatomist. After holding various positions the opportunity occurred for his promotion by the Venetian senate to the Chair of Anatomy at Padua where he thus became the successor to Vesalius, Fallopius, Fabricius and others. By his many descriptions of new forms of disease Morgagni made pathology a genuine branch of medicine. *78*

William Thomas Green Morton (1819-1868). Dentist, who while studying medicine with Dr. Chas. T. Jackson, a chemist of ability, learned of the anesthetic effects of chloric ether and later of sulphuric ether. In October, 1846, he persuaded Dr. John Collins Warren of the Massachusetts General Hospital to use the anesthetic. One month later the discovery was announced to the world by Henry J. Bigelow in the *Boston Medical and Surgical Journal*. It was due to the reputation of Warren and Bigelow that ether anesthesia was taken up all over the world. Morton himself tried to patent the drug, quarreled with Jackson about legal rights, and made no announcement until 1847. *110*

William Parry Murphy (1892-   ). American physician. Prominent for his work in demonstrating the effectiveness of liver in pernicious anemia. *141*

University of Naples. Founded by the Emperor Frederick II in the year 1225. In 1231 its faculty of medicine was abolished, but this was reconstituted in 1266. *46*

Albert Neisser (1855-1916). He discovered, in 1879, the organism causing gonorrhea, the gonococcus. *138*

Nero (37-68 A. D.). Roman emperor, 54 to 68 A. D. One of the most infamous of the emperors. Said to have deliberately caused the great conflagration of Rome. *35*

Sir Isaac Newton (1642-1727). English physicist. After publishing many papers on the science of optics, including the discovery of the composition of white light, Halley read before the Royal Society on the 21st of April, 1686, Newton's discourse concerning gravity and its causes, stating that the law of the inverse square "is the principle on which Mr. Newton has made out all the phenomena of the celestial motions so easily and naturally that its truth is past dispute." The anecdote concerning the tree and the apple is due to Voltaire, who had it from Newton's favorite niece Catherine Barton. *66*

Charles Nicolle (1866-   ). French physician. He demonstrated in 1909 that the body louse is the agent which transmits typhus fever. In the same year, John F. Anderson and Joseph Goldberger produced successful inoculations of typhus from man to monkey. *133*

Florence Nightingale (1820-1910). From her earliest youth she had a natural shrinking from society and the contacts which her social position gave her. She obtained for herself the best possible training available, in both England and Paris, concerning the management of hospitals and the care of patients. By the time of the Crimean War, 1854, she already had at home a reputation for her work in reorganizing hospitals. The condition of the barrack hospital at Scutari was so terrible that a royal commission was appointed, and the Secretary of War invited Miss Nightingale to proceed to the Crimea. She gave herself body and soul to the work, even by her presence and sympathy doing much to improve the morale of the wounded. *96*

Max Nitze (1848-1906). In 1877 he introduced the cystoscope and thus vastly improved the surgery of the bladder. *126*

Joseph P. O'Dwyer (1841-1898). Physician of Cleveland, Ohio, who perfected the method of intubation or insertion of a tube in the larynx or into the trachea when cut open. The method permits the continued passage of air and is used especially in diphtheria when the air passages are occluded. O'Dwyer takes his place alongside of Semmelweis and Credé as one of the great benefactors of infant life. *118*

Masaki Ogata (see article on **Kitasato**). *133*

Sir James Paget (1814-1899). British surgeon. Regius professor of physics at Cambridge. During his earlier years his progress in medicine was handicapped by his extreme poverty. When appointed professor at the College of Surgeons, he began giving his lectures in surgical pathology which did for pathology in England what Rudolph Virchow had done for it in Germany. He was, however, still poor. Probably no other famous surgeon waited longer for his work to come back to him, corresponding in this respect with John Hunter, whose place in English pathology he filled. The turn of the tide came just before 1858, when he was appointed surgeon extraordinary to Queen Victoria and later surgeon to the Prince of Wales. He then had for many years the largest surgical practice in London, working seldom less than sixteen or seventeen hours a day. *126*

Paracelsus (1493-1541). Son of Wilhelm Bombast von Hohenheim, a Swiss physician. He probably invented his name in order to denote his personal superiority to Celsus. At an early age he commenced questioning the value of the knowledge he was expected to acquire. He attacked the great authorities, Galen and Avicenna, and particularly the Galenic pharmacopoeia. *51*

Ambroise Paré (1510-1590). One of the greatest surgeons of all time and the most popular and lovable man of his age. He spent the greater part of his life with the armies in the continuous wars which during the 16th century nearly ruined France. Surgeon to four kings of France, he was beloved by friend and enemy alike, and in an age when obsequiousness was necessary for the preservation of life itself, Paré had a remarkably independent and straightforward manner and great pride in his calling. His works may be read in a complete edition (J. F. Malgaigne: *Œuvres complètes d'Ambroise Paré,* Paris, 1840) or in an abbreviated edition by Stephen Paget: *Ambroise Paré and His Times,* London, 1897. *51*

James Parkinson (1755-1824). A pupil of John Hunter and known principally for his work in paleontology, his contribution to the study of fossil remains placing him along with Avicenna, Fracastorius, Huxley, and others, as one of the medical men who made valuable contributions to this subject. He is known in medicine for his unique and classic description of *paralysis agitans* or Parkinson's disease, characterized by disturbances of movement and a tremor usually most marked in the hands. *102*

Louis Pasteur (1822-1895). Brilliant French chemist and with Koch the founder of bacteriology. In the elementary schools he entirely failed to distinguish himself, and when he attained his baccalaureate degree, a note was attached to his diploma to the effect that he was only mediocre in chemistry. He was stimulated to serious study of chemistry by Dumas's lectures at the Sorbonne. The first instance of the existence of chemical compounds with identical composition but absolutely different behavior, namely, the two tartaric acids deposited from wine lees, was as yet unexplained. Pasteur proved that inactivity of the one acid depended upon its being composed of equal parts of dextro- and levo-rotary acids, and thus by a single step he gained a place of honor among the chemists of the day and was immediately appointed Professor of Chemistry at Strassburg. His continued interest in these acids led to the commencement of his researches on fermentation. He had now become a leading man of science and was appointed professor and dean at the University of Lille, stating in his inaugural address that "in the field of observation chance favors only those who are prepared." Here he began the researches which exploded the notion of spontaneous generation and made him the acknowledged head of the greatest scientific movement of the time. He was installed at the Ecole normale in Paris, but not without opposition, even among his friends, who publicly announced that the problem he had set himself was unsolvable. He next turned his attention to a fatal disease of the silkworm which was ruining the French silk producers. The history of his investigation and gradual elimination of the unimportant conditions and recognition of those which controlled the disease illustrate his powers of conducting research and of quick and exact observation. Thomas Huxley had estimated in his own time the value of Pasteur's discoveries to the agricultural industries, including prevention of chicken cholera and anthrax, as sufficient to cover the whole cost of the war indemnity paid by France to Germany in 1870. Pasteur's work on rabies constitutes a no less interesting chapter in the study of disease. The practice of inoculation for hydrophobia was begun in 1885. *126*

Samuel Pepys (1633-1703). English diarist. He began on the first of January, 1660, his hidden life as a diarist. He would be notable for his interest in music and his presidency of the Royal Society, even if the diary had never been written. As a public servant in the capacity of what would now be known as permanent Under-Secretary of the Navy and later Secretary of the Admiralty, his diligence was rewarded with success. The diary has three qualities which are rarely found in perfection even when separated and which nowhere else appear in combination: it was secret, it was complete, and it was honest. Written in cipher, it is a human document of tremendous vitality. *72*

Sir William Henry Perkins (1838-1907). English chemist. He was early appointed an assistant in the research laboratory at the Royal College of Chemistry and devoted his evenings to studying in a laboratory fitted up in his home. In trying artificially to produce quinine, he came upon a method of making aniline black and later aniline blue. Then, as a boy of eighteen, he left the College and, with the aid of his father and brother, erected a dye works for the manufacture of this newly discovered coloring matter (1857). This date marks the foundation of the coal tar industry. *118*

Max Joseph von Pettenkofer (1818-1901). Shortly after graduation in medicine, he was appointed professor of dietetic chemistry, and later professor of hygiene, at Munich, when under his direction the first Hygienic Institute was opened. He thus became the founder of experimental hygiene. He is famous for his work in practical hygiene, particularly in connection with water supplies and sewage disposal. *123*

Philippe Pinel (1745-1826). French physician, born and educated in the south of France, whence he removed to Paris, finally becoming head physician of the Bicêtre and later the Salpêtrière Hospital in Paris. His fame rests entirely upon the innovation of treating insane people as patients rather than as prisoners. *89*

Joseph Priestley (1733-1804). English chemist whose life was largely taken up in performing the duties of a non-conformist minister. He was interested in studying the properties of various gases. As a result of his experiments with what was later known as oxygen, he concluded that it was not the common air, but a substance "in much greater perfection" which rendered common air respirable and made it support combustion. He was convinced of the analogy between respiration and combustion and showed that growing plants restore air which has been vitiated. *80*

François Rabelais (1490-1553). French humorist, humanist, and physician. His two great works, *Gargantua* and *Pantagruel,* keenly ridiculed the medieval custom of "stuffing the youthful mind" with book learning and advocated a much broader education. They were, however, written for a popular audience whose speech and thought were then so coarse as to be even unintelligible at the present time. Notwithstanding the high literary character of the two works and the frequency with which passages in them are cited, their archaic language make them unreadable today. *51*

Sir William Read. Commenced life as a tailor, but in 1694 set himself up as an oculist, after having hired someone to write a book on the subject under his own name. His success attracted the attention of Queen Anne, and he was actually knighted. Swift and other coffee-house wits made much fun of him. *92*

Major Walter Reed (1851-1902). Surgeon, U. S. Army Medical Corps. Reed was appointed in 1900 head of a commission to study yellow fever in Cuba, then occupied by the American army. Carlos Finlay of Havana had already nineteen years previously, at an international conference, advanced the theory that the disease was transmitted by the *stegomyia fasciata,* a black mosquito with silvery markings. He was, however, looked upon as visionary until after the work of the army board, in one of the most brilliant and conclusive researches in the history of medical science. They found that the virus of yellow fever is transmitted by the *stegomyia fasciata.* Incidentally, they found that although uninfected mosquitoes bite day and night, the infected mosquito does not bite except at night, thus explaining the impunity with which Europeans may visit an infected district in the daytime provided they do not sleep there at night. In its severer forms yellow fever is one of the most fatal of epidemic diseases, the mortality ranging from 15 per cent. to 85 per cent. *98*

Rembrandt Harmens Van Rijn (1606-1669). Dutch painter whose position in European art rests in the originality of his mind, the power of his imagination, the boldness of his system of light and shade, and his intense humanity. He lived at a time when Holland had entered on her great career of national enterprise. Early in life he achieved the position of first portrait painter of Amsterdam. He had many friends, pupils, and numerous commissions. In his large house he gathered a considerable collection of paintings and engravings, but in later years the long-continued wars, the civil troubles of the country, and the scarcity of money brought Rembrandt into poverty. Finally, his entire collection was sold by the Insolvency Chamber, at a time unfavorable all over the world, for the sum of five thousand gilders. The collection of Charles I of England, sold about the same time, also brought a comparatively small sum. *66*

Roger of Palermo. Surgeon of the school of Salerno. Wrote his *Practica* in 1170. *44*

Philippe Ricord (1799-1889). A native of Baltimore, he was the greatest authority on venereal diseases after John Hunter. He was instrumental in correcting the erroneous belief, due to Hunter, as to the identity of gonorrhea and syphilis. Dr. Oliver Wendell Holmes styled him "the Voltaire of pelvic literature—a skeptic as to the morality of the race in general, who would have submitted Diana to treatment with his mineral specifics and ordered a course of blue pills for the vestal virgins." *138*

Rhazes (860-932). A great clinician who practiced with distinction in Bagdad. The first of the Arabs to treat medicine in a comprehensive and encyclopedic manner. *42*

William Konrad Röntgen (1845-1922). Röntgen was educated at Utrecht but showed no particular talent until he came under the influence of Clausius. At Würzburg, while experimenting with a Crookes' tube, he noticed accidental shadows of solid substances. He communicated the discovery to the Würzburg Society in 1895, calling them "X rays." They were immediately recognized as being useful in medicine and surgery and the name "Röntgen rays" was proposed. He became successively the professor of physics at Strassburg, Giessen, Würzburg and, finally, at Munich. Röntgen was much saddened by the war, the outcome of which he had predicted, and died a lonely and isolated man. *135*

Eucharious Roslin. He wrote *Rosengarten* (1513), the only textbook on obstetrics during the Renaissance. *52*

Sir Ronald Ross (1857-1932). While in the Indian medical service he located the Anopheles mosquito as the intermediate host in the transmission of malaria. In 1902 he received the Nobel Prize for his work in the reduction of malarial fever, work which has resulted in its effective prevention all over the world. *133*

Jean Jacques Rousseau (1712-1778). French philosopher who spent the greater part of his life being annoyed by his enemies and suspecting his friends. As a result of his peculiar temperament and his writings, he had to submit to a great deal of persecution which he endured much less well than did other writers of his time. Rousseau was a sincere republican who saw clearly that the monarchical system resulted in the greatest misery for the greatest number. His influence has been greatest as an exponent rather than as an originator of ideas, and his success lay largely in the excellence with which he was able to describe the human passions and the beauties of nature. The color and tone resulting from this combination of the effect of nature on the feelings and of the feelings on the appreciation of nature leave him unrivaled in literary history. 77

Pierre Paul Emil Roux (see article on **Emil von Behring**). *130*

The Royal Society. The Royal Society of London for Improving Natural Knowledge is one of the oldest of its kind in Europe. Its charter of incorporation passed the Great Seal in 1662. During its early existence, it commenced the publication of *The Philosophical Transactions,* a publication, now as then, of world-wide celebrity. The Royal Society has often been turned to by the government for information concerning scientific undertakings of importance such as the protection of buildings and ships from lightning, measurement of latitude, the various antarctic and arctic expeditions, tidal observations, telegraphic communication, meteorological administration, deep-sea research and color blindness. The Society is the custodian of the imperial standard yard and pound, it controls the National Physical Laboratory, the Kew Observatory and is represented on the governing boards of many important scientific and educational institutions. *83*

Benjamin Rush (1745-1813). A Quaker physician of Philadelphia who, after education at Princeton, in London, and in Paris, began practice in Philadelphia at the age of twenty-four. Benjamin Rush is one of the signers of the Declaration of Independence. During the yellow fever epidemic of 1793 Rush was active in caring for the sick, his account of the epidemic being very realistic. Although his therapeutic ideas were most arbitrary, he was undoubtedly the ablest clinician of his time. *90*

Salem Witchcraft Episode (1691-1692). A remarkable outburst of fanaticism which probably went farther than it would have, had it not been for the influence of Cotton Mather. Witchcraft is a term applied particularly in Europe to the "black" magic of women. Though early in the 13th Century the real existence of magic was held in doubt, from then until the 15th Century the Inquisition instilled in the popular mind a conception of the rise and development of witchcraft, and after that time we have a period of witch persecution. On the Continent of Europe the witchcraft cases were taken out of the hands of the Inquisition at the beginning of the 16th Century. Trials and executions did not finally cease until the end of the 18th Century, and in Spanish America not until well into the 19th Century. The total number of victims has been variously estimated at from hundreds of thousands to several million people. *83*

School of Salerno. A secular institution probably originating in the 8th Century and early making its city known as the "Civitas Hippocratica." The school had a great reputation until the 12th or 13th Century, when the introduction of Arabian medicine and the rise of the University of Montpellier were gradually fatal to it. It was closed by Napoleon in 1811. *44*

Antonio Scarpa (1747-1832). Venetian anatomist famous for his genius and the accuracy with which he portrayed details as shown in the pen drawings illustrating his works, the greatest of which, the *Tabule nevrologicæ* gives, among other things, the first delineation of the nerves of the heart. *102*

Fritz Schaudinn (1871-1906). German zoölogist who devoted his life to the study of the protozoa. His discovery of the causative agent in syphilis, the Spirochaeta pallida, was preceded by other important contributions to medicine, such as the discovery of the entamoeba causing dysentery, the identification of the cause of Tertian malaria and of hookworm infection.

Schaudinn became director of Protozoölogy at the Kaiserliches Gesundheitsampt and later of the Institute for Naval and Tropical Hygiene in Hamburg. *138*

Karl Wilhelm Scheele (1742-1786). Swedish chemist. He began life as an apothecary's assistant spending most of his time, however, in the experimental examination of the substances with which he had to deal. In spite of business cares, he found time for an enormous amount of original research and his power as an experimental investigator and an accurate observer has seldom been surpassed. His work evidences a careful plan laid out to settle points and verify inferences which he had made. He had the type of mind which left nothing in doubt if an experiment could decide it and he never felt that he had investigated any compound fully until he could both unmake and re-make it. Perhaps no man surpasses him as a discoverer of new substances. *78*

Theodor Schwann (1810-1882). German physiologist who inherited his father's taste for mathematics. Schwann's most valuable work was done, not during the many years that he was professor at Louvain and Liége, but while he was an assistant of Müller at Berlin. While Müller was preparing his book on physiology, he made the histological discovery that the nerve fiber has an envelope which now bears his name. The whole germ theory of Pasteur, as well as the antiseptic theory of Lister, may be traced to his influence, for he was able to prove as early as 1836 that putrefaction was due to living bodies and discovered the organic nature of yeast. His generalization on the cell theory became the foundation of modern histology and thus opened the way for the work of Rudolph Virchow. *104*

Ignatz Philipp Semmelweis (1818-1865). Hungarian physician who became assistant professor in the Maternity Department at Vienna under Johann Klein. His failure to find a satisfactory explanation for the high mortality in such causes as overcrowding, fear, etc., led eventually to recognition of the essential nature of puerperal infection and its practical eradication by the introduction of an antiseptic technique. Semmelweis was ridiculed and persecuted and finally driven from Vienna by Klein and other jealous and reactionary individuals. He was appointed to the Maternity Department in Pest where he succeeded in reducing the mortality to 0.85%. The strain of controversy and his sensitiveness to persecution brought on insanity, and he soon thereafter died. *113*

Michael Servetus (1511-1553). A man with marked individuality in his religious views, who, in spite of his intense biblicism and passionate devotion to the person of Christ, held views abhorrent to both Catholics and Protestants alike. In 1545 he opened the fatal correspondence with John Calvin by forwarding him the manuscript of a much enlarged revision of his theological tracts, from which it was decided that he should be exterminated, and after many months of escapes and wanderings over Europe he was finally recognized in a church in Geneva and immediately arrested, tried, and burned at the stake. *56*

James Marion Sims (1813-1883). American gynecologist. He hit upon the lateral posture known as the Sims' position which, with other inventions, led to his success in operating for vesicovaginal fistula. He visited Europe in 1861 and performed the operation before leading French surgeons and was soon in request all over Europe as an operator in diseases of women. He was one of the most original and gifted of American surgeons. *112*

Sir James Young Simpson (1811-1870). Scottish obstetrician. He was present in 1846 at an operation in which sulphuric ether was used and he immediately began to employ it in obstetrics. The next year he read a paper on chloroform in which he detailed the use of anesthetics from the earliest times, but especially dwelt upon the advantages of chloroform. Because of his great ability and fascinating personality, he had an enormous practice, being one of the most remarkable personalities of his time. *110*

William Smellie (1697-1763). English obstetrician who introduced various improvements in forceps and laid down safe rules for their use. His illustrations of natural and pathological labors are of classical value and he was responsible for differentiating between normal and contracted pelves by actual measurement. *78*

Nathan Smith (1762-1829). He built up the Dartmouth School of Medicine, then established a similar department at Yale, then at Bowdoin, and later at the University of Vermont. *102*

Theobald Smith (1859-   ). Director of the Department of Animal Pathology of the Rockefeller Institute for Medical Research, and one of the most distinguished American pathologists. He early showed that immunization could be obtained by the injection of filtrates of bacterial cultures, thus antedating Behring, Roux and others in this field. His work on the parasite of Texas Fever and the tracing of its transmission by the cattle tick did much to advance the science of protozoan diseases.

He was the first to differentiate clearly between the causative agents of bovine and human tuberculosis. *133*

Soranus of Ephesus (98-138). Greek physician living during the reigns of the emperors Trajan and Hadrian. By his treatise on midwifery and diseases of women, he is our leading authority on the gynecology, obstetrics and pediatrics, of antiquity. *52*

Edward Robinson Squibb (1819-1900). American physician and chemist, and founder of the Laboratories which bear his name.

In 1845 he graduated from Jefferson Medical College and received the appointment of demonstrator of anatomy, librarian and curator of the museum and clerk of the clinics at the college.

Because of his special interest in the purity and general quality of medicinal supplies, he was called by the United States Government, in 1852, to establish and serve as director of a Laboratory in connection with the Naval Hospital, Brooklyn Navy Yard. During the five years in this capacity, his scientific investigations covered a wide range and included the development of processes for the manufacture of fluid extracts, assaying potent tinctures, and the establishment of standards and specifications for medical supplies, many of which have remained unchanged up to the present time. The difficulty of obtaining appropriations for the continuance of this work and the urging of members of the medical profession caused him to resign and establish (in 1858) his own laboratories;

a move which was made just in time to enable him to render greater service to the armies during the Civil War.

He published altogether nearly one hundred papers on the standardization and purification of medicinal products. This work was of material aid in the establishment of standards for the U. S. P. preparations, and, as a member of the U. S. Pharmacopoeia Revision Committee, he took a most active part in the development and improvement of the Materia Medica as described in the U. S. Pharmacopoeia. *vii, 112*

Ernest Henry Starling (1866-1927). One of the foremost of English physiologists, and after Harvey the one who has done the most to advance our knowledge of the action of the heart. Starling was early attracted to physiology as a career, but lack of funds and the inadequate academic facilities of the time nearly diverted him from this career.

Commencing at Guy's Hospital, the equipment and funds were both inadequate and so he carried on some of his work at Schaefer's Laboratory at University College where he met Bayliss, also working in the Laboratory. Together they began a scientific partnership which lasted for thirty years. Although both possessed scientific imagination of the highest order, Starling was more forceful and perhaps less skillful with technical procedure.

The equipment at Guy's Hospital steadily improved, for it became generally recognized that Starling was going to be a great man. Indeed, not long after the opening of new laboratories at the hospital he became Professor of Physiology at the University College where the previous experience in organizing the hospital laboratories was useful in the development of the Institute of Physiology, laboratories which became a great center of activity.

Some of Starling's best and earliest work was done in elucidating the mechanism of the flow of lymph. With Bayliss he then undertook a study of the movements of the intestines and then of pancreatic secretion. He then turned again to a study of blood flow using the now famous device known as the Starling heart-lung preparation. His *Principles of Human Physiology* is one of the best textbooks on the subject in the English language. *140*

Robert Stevenson (1772-1850). Scottish engineer who, as engineer to the Commissioners of Northern Lighthouses, designed and executed among others the important lighthouse on Bell Rock. He introduced improved methods of lighthouse illumination including intermittent and flashing lights and the mast lanterns of light ships. In the capacity of civil engineer, he built harbors, docks, breakwaters and improved river and canal navigation and constructed several important bridges. It is due to him that malleable iron was introduced to replace cast iron for railways and it was by his interposition that the Admiralty Sailing Directions for the coasts and waters of Great Britain have been prepared. *78*

Jan Swammerdan (1637-1680). Dutch naturalist. Son of an apothecary and naturalist. Devoted his time to human anatomy and to the anatomy of may-flies and bees. *72*

Thomas Sydenham (1624-1689). English physician whose reputation as the Father of English Medicine dates rather from a later appreciation of his attitude towards the patient than from any appraisal of his contemporaries, save perhaps one or two of the most talented of them. He did the best he could for his patients and did much to improve the ethics of practice and to rationalize the treatment of disease. *74*

Jacques Dubois (Sylvius) (1478-1555). We are assured by Vesalius, who was once his pupil, that he never advanced science or rectified the mistakes of his predecessors. He had a coarseness of manner and language that could hardly be tolerated even in the rude state of his times. *60*

Theodoric, Bishop of Cervia (1205-1296). One of the most original and clear-thinking surgeons of all times. *46*

Diego Rodriguez de Silva y Velazquez (1599-1660). One of the greatest painters the world has known. His paintings escaped the rapacity of the French marshals. Ruskin says of him that "Everything Velazquez does may be taken as absolutely right by the student." In the year 1624 Velazquez received three hundred ducats from King Philip IV to pay the cost of the removal of his family to Madrid, where he remained for the rest of his life. For thirty-six years the King remained his faithful and attached friend. Velazquez's association with the royal household, as well as the enthusiastic contemporary recognition of his genius, placed him in a position of financial ease. At the consummation of peace between France and Spain celebrated by the marriage of the Infanta Maria Theresa to Louis XIV, Velazquez, in the midst of the grandees of the two first Courts of Christendom, attracted much attention by his noble bearing and the splendor of his costume. *66*

Andreas Vesalius (1514-1564). A native of Brussels. The most commanding figure in European medicine after Galen and before Harvey. The difficulties surrounding the practical pursuit of anatomy in France were such as to lead him to Italy, where in his twenty-second year he commenced publicly to demonstrate at the

MYSTERY, MAGIC, AND MEDICINE

University of Padua. He went subsequently, by express invitation, to Bologna and to Pisa. He was the first of an illustrious line of teachers by whom the reputation of the Italians in anatomy was raised in the 16th Century to the greatest eminence. *51*

Rudolph Virchow (1821-1902). German pathologist. He was very early appointed assistant prosector at the Charité Hospital in Berlin and founded the Archiv für pathologische Anatomie and Physiologie which is everywhere known as Virchow's Archiv. About this time he was obliged to leave Berlin because he showed no political sympathy with the revolutionary tendencies of the time, and was given a professorship at Würzburg, which institution was made famous by his labors. In 1856 he was recalled to Berlin as Professor of Anatomy and Director of the Pathological Institute. His views that every animal is constituted of a sum of vital units or cells, each of which manifests the characteristics of life, has dominated the theory of disease since the middle of the 19th Century, when he enunciated it. By his book on Cellular Pathology he established what Lister has described as the "true and fertile doctrine that every morbid structure consists of cells which have been derived from pre-existing cells as progeny." Virchow, besides founding the subject of cellular pathology upon which the very existence of modern medicine is based, did much to put anthropology on a sound critical basis. *93*

Carl von Voit (1831-1908). German physiologist. He was an extremely important link in the continuity of the chain of investigators who have elucidated our modern conception of the science of nutrition. A pupil of Liebig, he was the teacher and inspiration of an illustrious line of successors, Rubner, Atwater, Friedrich Müller, E. Voit, Kramer, Lusk, Cathcarte. Berthelot, a co-worker of Lavoisier and instructor in chemistry of Napoleon I, bequeathed his sword to his famous pupil Gay-Lussac. Liebig owed much to the instruction and friendship of Gay-Lussac. Thus the line of descent is complete. *123*

Alessandro Volta (1745-1827). Italian physicist and pioneer in the study of electrical phenomena. Napoleon had him, by invitation, to Paris to show his experiments on contact electricity. It was Volta who differentiated electrolytes from other conductors and showed that a difference of potential is created by the mere contact of two such conductors. His name is used to denote the unit of measure of electric potential, the volt. *78*

François Marie Arouet de Voltaire (1694-1778). French philosopher and man of letters. Born without the name Voltaire he early showed a propensity for writing lampoons and libels which finally got him into prison in the Bastille, where he decided to change his name. He wrote between fifty and sixty different pieces for the theatre of which the best were comedies, although his tragedies are of extraordinary merit. The bare names of his poems constitute a catalog of fourteen royal octavo volumes. His writings are characterized by an almost superhuman cleverness. He was perhaps not aware of the fact, or at least it did not bother him, that in politics his attacks on the state of things were destructive without offering any substitute. The matter about which he wrote is not of great value, but in literary craftsmanship and form he has had no superior. *77*

Augustus Volney Waller (1816-1870). English histologist who by making microscopic preparations of sections of nerve trunks and of the spinal cord showed that after experimentally cutting either, a degeneration takes place in that portion of the fiber distal from the nerve cell. This fact, established in 1852, has become known as Waller's Law or Wallerian Degeneration. The investigations of Waller were the starting point of our present conception of the structure of the nervous system. *119*

Joshua Ward (1685-1781). Also known as "Spot" Ward, because of a mark on one side of his face. He made his fortune by the sale of antimonial pills, a "dropsy purging powder," "Ward's paste," and Ward's "essence for headaches." After the Parliamentary Act of 1748 he was specially exempted from the penalties of that act restricting the practice of medicine. He was impudent enough to request burial in Westminster Abbey, and Pope said of him:

> *"Of late, without the least pretence to skill,*
> *Ward's grown a famed physician by a pill."* 90

August von Wassermann (1866-1925). Although he has made many contributions to the sciences of bacteriology and protozoan diseases, he is best known for the blood test for syphilis named for him, a discovery that was made one year after Schaudinn had found the parasite of the disease.

The Wassermann test depends upon the power of an unknown substance in the syphilitic serum to combine with a suitable antigen, the combination using up more or less "complement" which has been supplied in definite quantities. As the result of the exhaustion of the complement, when blood cells and a hemo-lyzing serum are subsequently added, there is insufficient complement left to enable hemolysis to take place, hence a positive test. *138*

James Watt (1736-1819). Scottish engineer and inventor of the modern condensing steam engine. The engines then in use were almost inconceivably clumsy and wasteful of fuel. In 1764 Watt was given a model of an engine to repair and was so struck with its enormous consumption of steam that he determined to find the cause and the remedy. Various difficulties prevented the introduction of the improvements which he invented. Finally, he formed a partnership with a wealthy business man by the name of Boulton who had the good sense to leave inventing to his partner and the capacity to make the business a commercial success. *78*

Ernst Heinrich Weber (1795-1878). Professor of anatomy and physiology at Leipzig. He was especially famous for his researches into aural and cutaneous sensations, and applying to them the idea of measurement, thus generalizing his results in Weber's Law, which states that sensation increases in arithmetic progression as the stimulus increases in geometric progression. In other words, in order to appreciate an increase in sensation, the stimulus must bear a certain fixed proportion to the immediately preceding stimulus. The law holds true only within certain limits and most exactly interprets the facts in the case of hearing, sight, pressure, and muscular sense. Weber's brother, Eduard Friedrich Weber (1806-1871), collaborated with him in a number of his physiological investigations. Another brother, Wilhelm Eduard Weber (1804-1891), was Professor of Physics at Göttingen and built in 1833 the first electro-magnetic telegraph. *106*

Horace Wells (1815-1848). A dentist of Hartford, Conn., who began to use nitrous oxide and communicated with his former partner, Dr. Wm. T. G. Morton, about the merits of anesthesia. Subsequently, however, he had a death under anesthesia and eventually committed suicide. *109*

George Hoyt Whipple (1878-   ). American pathologist. Prominent for his work in tuberculosis, black-water fever, anemia and pigment metabolism. *141*

Fernand Widal (1862-1929). French physician, "standard bearer of French medicine." As a pupil he collaborated with Chantemesse in his early work on prophylactic vaccination for typhoid fever. He is well known for the phenomenon bearing his name, the agglutination of typhoid bacteria by the serum of typhoid patients. *129*

Aloes. A purgative substance which was used by the Greeks and probably by the Egyptians.

Aneurism. A circumscribed enlargement, usually of one of the large arteries, due to injury and failure of its wall. We have descriptions of aneurism from the time of Galen. Morgagni recognized syphilis as a possible cause.

GLOSSARY OF MEDICAL TERMS

Anthrax. An acute infectious disease caused by the anthrax bacillus. In animals the disease is widespread, much more so in Europe and Asia than in America. The disease is always serious, and recovery from the internal forms is rare. Animals can be temporarily immunized against the disease by Pasteur's method of vaccination. Massive doses of immune serum are also used for the treatment of human beings.

Benzoin. An East Indian balsamic resin. Mildly irritant and antiseptic in character and therefore employed in chronic inflammations and for the healing of ulcers.

Bone of Luz. Mentioned in the Talmud as one of the bones lying somewhere in the spinal column and forming an indestructible nucleus from which the body could be raised from the dead at the resurrection. It plays a part in ancient medieval medicine.

Bubonic Plague (Black Death). The specific infectious disease caused by the bacillus pestis. Since the great epidemic of Justinian in the 6th Century, there have occurred many epidemics of varying severity in Europe. Of these the famous black death of the 14th Century, which first appeared in 1348, resulted in the extinction of one-quarter of the population of the world or some sixty millions of people. Epidemics continued in Europe to the end of the 18th Century and waned throughout the world progressively in the 19th Century so that it appeared to belong to the diseases of the past. Its reappearance and spread over various parts of the world in the 20th Century is one of the most ominous facts in modern epidemiology, the deaths probably exceeding ten millions of people. The disease is carried by rats and transferred to man by the bite of fleas. Its existence has been maintained in certain portions of Central Asia by native rodents since time immemorial.

Caduceus. The Greek god Aesculapius is always shown with a staff and serpent, which in conventional form is known as the "caduceus." The true caduceus comprises a single serpent and a staff. The winged staff, bearing two serpents symmetrically twined thereon, as used by the U. S. Army Medical Corps, is not the caduceus but is the emblem of Mercury, the Greek God Hermes, the Messenger of the Gods, and the deity who was said to preside over thieves, merchants, and orators.

Camphor. A product of a tree flourishing in Japan, Formosa, and Central China. A mildly irritant and antiseptic agent principally used in liniments. Used in the Orient before the dawn of history, it was introduced into Europe in the Middle Ages.

Cholera. An acute infectious disease characterized by profuse, effortless diarrhea, vomiting, and colitis. The disease is of great antiquity, having existed in India from time immemorial, but it did not appear in other countries until modern times, when the first great epidemic occurred in 1817 throughout Asia and Africa.

Cinnamon. The inner bark of a small evergreen tree native to Ceylon. Known from remote antiquity. Used as a volatile flavoring oil and as a disinfectant in dentistry.

Cloves. Dried unexpanded flower buds of an evergreen tree native to the East Indies and one of the principal Oriental spices. It formed the basis of a lucrative trade early in the Christian Era.

Cubebs. Fruit of a species of pepper native to the Indian Archipelago. Introduced in medicine by Arabian physicians.

Digitalis. Dried leaves of the foxglove. Known as a poison and described and pictured by Dioscorides. The first mention by medical writers is by the Bavarian physician, Leonhard Fuchs (1542), Professor of Medicine at Tübingen. First brought prominently to the notice of the medical profession by Dr. W. Withering in his *Account of the Foxglove* (1785).

Diphtheria (see article on **Emil von Behring**). An acute infectious disease caused by the diphtheria bacillus and characterized by the formation of fibrinous exudates, usually upon the membranes of the throat, and by constitutional symptoms due to the absorption of the toxins produced by the bacteria. Although the disease is referred to in the Babylonian Talmud, it was first accurately described by Aretæus. Very serious epidemics were described in different portions of Europe during the 16th, 17th, and 18th centuries. In recent years, in certain large communities, the disease has been practically eradicated by the active immunization of young children with toxin-antitoxin or toxoid.

Dysentery. A disease caused either by bacteria (bacillary dysentery) or a protozoan organism (amœbic dysentery). Hippocrates discussed the various aspects of dysentery, and Galen gave it its present connotation; that is, a disease in which there is passage of bloody stools containing mucus and accompanied by tenesmus or cramps. In amœbic dysentery the symptoms are usually intermittent.

Ginger. A very important item in the commerce between Europe and the East during the Middle Ages. Rated next in value to pepper. Known from remote antiquity in India and supposed by the Greeks and Romans to be a product of southern Arabia.

Gout. An inflammation of the joints which may be either acute or chronic and in which there is a deposition of sodium urate crystals in the joints and tissues. Thomas Sydenham was the first to distinguish the disease from other joint diseases, and his description is the masterpiece on which subsequent accounts are based. There is a direct relation between gout, alcoholism, and overeating. The disease is rare in women.

Malaria. A disease acquired by the bite of an infected mosquito and characterized by paroxysms of intermittent fever. A good description of malaria was given by Hippocrates.

Mandragora. Mandrake root is one of the plants of the family yielding belladonna alkaloids. The deadly Nightshade, belonging to the same family, although known to the ancients, was less extensively employed as a medicine until recent times. The principal constituents of the Mandrake root are hyoscyamine and scopolamine.

Atropa Mandragora is native to the Mediterranean region. It was recognized as a medicine by all ancient writers and in the Middle Ages achieved a tremendous reputation for magical power. Rachel sought Mandrakes of Leah, possibly to ease the pains of childbirth. Dioscorides was the first to recommend wine of Mandragora for surgical anesthesia. He identified the drug with a root named after the Enchantress Circe. Shakespeare alludes to the plant in *Antony and Cleopatra,* and in *Romeo and Juliet.* The plant was supposed to cure maniacs, and the legends about the human shape of the root of the plant, its shrieks when uprooted, and the risk supposed to be run in destroying it, are common features of English and German folk-lore.

Meningitis. Epidemic cerebral spinal fever is an inflammation of the coverings of the brain and spinal cord caused by the meningococcus. It was first described in a small outbreak in Geneva in 1805. Since then there have been extensive outbreaks in the United States and in Europe. The disease occurs both in epidemic and sporadic forms. Before the use of anti-meningococcic serum, the mortality rate was over 70 per cent.

Musk. The most valuable is the Tong-king musk from Central China. It gives strength and permanency to vegetable essences and compounded perfumes.

Essential Nephritis or Bright's Disease. Bright included in his clinical category all the affections of the kidney associated with dropsy and albumin in the urine. The essential Bright's Disease, however, is now understood as primarily an involvement of the gomeruli with secondary contraction of the kidney but without increase in blood pressure. The contracted kidney due to arteriosclerosis and accompanied by cardiac dropsy is not in this category. The disease is a diffuse progressive degeneration of the kidney tissue which may be either on a degenerative basis or as a result of injury from toxins, infections, etc. It ranks high as a cause of death.

Opium. A narcotic drug prepared from the opium poppy, a plan now so widely distributed that its original habitat is in doubt. For the first twelve centuries of the Christian Era opium was obtained only from Asia Minor. Its first use was apparently as a medicine.

Pepper. A pungent spice native to the Indian Archipelago. It is one of the earliest used spices. Known to mankind for many ages it was long a staple article of commerce between India and Europe. The ransom of Rome was paid partly in pepper, and its value in the Middle Ages led the Portuguese to seek a sea route to India.

Quinine. The most important alkaloid of the bark of the Cinchona and chiefly valuable as a specific antidote to malaria. The first known instance of the use of Cinchona was in 1638, when the Countess of Chinchon, wife of the Governor of Peru, was cured of an attack of fever by its administration. Since the tree grows isolated in the dense tropical forest, the procuring, drying, and transporting of the product are operations laborious in the extreme.

Rabies (hydrophobia). An acute infectious disease of certain animals caused by a virus which can be communicated to man, usually by the bite of a rabid animal. When so communicated, a painful and fatal disease eventually results, unless the individual is protected by the prophylactic treatment of Pasteur or by modifications thereof.

Records of the disease have existed from the time of Aristotle. The preventive inoculation of dogs and rigid enforcement of muzzling laws has led to a practical eradication of the disease in certain countries.

Rhubarb. The name applies to both a vegetable and a drug. The drug is described as a Chinese herbal dating from 2700 B. C. and by Dioscorides as a root coming from beyond the Bosporus. Because of the difficulty of preserving it from insects while being carried from the East, it was formerly one of the most costly of drugs.

Scarlatina (Scarlet Fever). An acute infectious disease characterized by a sore throat and a punctate rash appearing first on the neck and behind the ears. In early times it was confounded with measles and rubella. The disease was first definitely described by Thomas Sydenham in 1675.

GLOSSARY OF MEDICAL TERMS

Scrofula. The name formerly given to the disease now called tuberculosis. Before the modern era the term was essentially applied to what was tuberculosis of the bones and lymphatic glands. The old English popular name was the "King's Evil"—so called from the belief that the sovereign's touch could effect a cure. This superstition dates back to the time of Edward the Confessor, and in France to a still earlier time.

Smallpox (distinguished by its epithet from the great pox or syphilis, introduced into Europe in 1498). A specific infectious disease caused by a filtrable virus present in the skin lesions. It was endemic in China and India many centuries before the birth of Christ. It has long been regarded as native to India and Central Africa. The first clear description was written by Rhazes in the 10th Century, *De Varioles et Morbillis.* In the 15th, 16th, 17th, and 18th centuries it was the cause of an enormous mortality in many European countries.

Syphilis. A disease of slow evolution caused by the *Spirochaeta Pallida.* Whether or not it was present in the Old World before the time of Columbus is not certain, but, at any rate, it was spread among the inhabitants of Barcelona by the Spanish sailors returning from America, and in 1493 it reached Italy, and in a few years the whole of Europe was aflame. At first it was called the Neapolitan Disease, then the French pox or grand pox; but in 1530 Fracastorius wrote a poem about it which gave it its present name. The venereal origin of the disease was not at first generally recognized. In the 20th Century the conception of the disease was greatly broadened and the great multiplicity of its clinical manifestations better understood. Mercury was early introduced as one of the important remedies, and treatment with a heavy metal is still regarded as essential for the best results. The possibility of curing the disease, however, first came with the introduction by Ehrlich of the arsenical compounds known now as arsphenamine and neoarsphenamine.

Tetanus. An acute infectious disease caused by the tetanus bacillus and usually resulting from the infection of puncture wounds, often trifling in character, with material contaminated with the organisms.

The disease was known to Hippocrates, who stated that "such persons as are seized with tetanus die within four days, or if they pass these, they recover." Prophylactic injections of antitoxin have greatly decreased the incidence and mortality from the disease.

Typhoid Fever. A general infection caused by the typhoid bacillus and characterized by hyperplasia and ulceration of the lymphoid tissue of the intestines, and a tendency to a continuously high fever. It is presumed that several disease pictures given by Hippocrates relate to cases of typhoid fever. The present name was first given to it by Pierre Louis, and as a consequence of the dissemination of the knowledge of his work by his pupils, the profession gradually became familiar with the disease.

Vitamins. Vitamins are essential food principles associated with the prevention of specific deficiency diseases, the promotion of optimum physical development, and the maintenance of optimum functional activity and resistance of specific body tissues. They are classified apart from the ordinary energy-producing and tissue-building nutrients.

The first of the vitamin deficiency diseases to be recognized was scurvy in which the affected tissues are the capillary vessels, the long bones and the bone marrow. It was cured with foods rich in Vitamin C, such as citrus fruits and certain fresh vegetables long before the existence of vitamins was suspected.

Vitamin B was discovered as a result of studies of the disease beri-beri which is characterized by degenerative changes in nerve tissue. More recently Vitamin B has been shown to bear a close relationship to growth, to the desire for food, and to gastro-intestinal function. Its richest sources are wheat germ and yeast.

Vitamin G (associated with the deficiency disease pellagra and concerned with the maintenance of a healthy condition of the skin and mucous surfaces) was at first not recognized as being distinct from Vitamin B. The two usually occur together but not in constant ratio.

The existence of Vitamins A and D, naturally abundant in fresh fish-liver oils, was only recognized much later and then as an outgrowth of extensive nutrition experiments in which certain feeding deficiencies had to be explained. The favorable influence of Vitamin A upon growth and its relation to resistance to infection were soon recognized and later more clearly understood in terms of the pronounced influence of this vitamin on the epithelial tissues and glandular organs throughout the body. It was only by destroying the Vitamin A in cod-liver oil, through oxidation, however, that it became evident that the oil contained still another vitamin, Vitamin D, essential for protection against rickets and the development of normal bone and tooth structure.